A Guide to the
Dragonfli
of Great Britain

DAN POWELL
Edited by Colin Twist

To my wife Rosemary

ISBN 1 900159 01 5

First published 1999

Arlequin Press, 26 Broomfield Road, Chelmsford, Essex CM1 1SW
Telephone: 01245 267771

© Arlequin Press
© All illustrations Dan Powell

A catalogue record for this book is available.

Contents

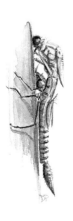

Acknowledgments

First and foremost I would like to thank my family, especially my wife who has "lived" Dragonflies for the last three years without ever complaining (except once in a bog in Scotland, mind you the cleggs were huge! So thanks to all you blood-suckers out there who have had hearty meals out of me). She has been the best company throughout the many miles we have travelled to see these beasties and even managed to take a brilliant set of photographs of all the resident species in a year, some sort of record surely?

Special thanks go to my friends Barry and Ingrid Duffin, John and Shirley Dodds, Colin and Angela Savage, Helen and Maggie next door, Melvyn Brickwood, Richard Carpenter, John Taverner and Pete Durnell. All have either helped with reference material, read copy, been good company on trips or endured endless monologues on Dragonflies. A project of this nature would have been impossible to undertake properly without the help and kind co-operation of many people, whose experience of Dragonflies is far greater than mine, I would like to thank Dave Winsland, Derek Moore, Bob and Betty Smith, David Clarke, Stewart Taylor and Tim Beynon for sharing their knowledge without question. Tim in particular has been a great help with this book and I hope he doesn't mind being regarded as a friend now.

Thanks to Colin Twist for his expert contribution to this book, it has been a pleasure to work with him. Many thanks also to Dean Hearn for his endless help with the setting of this book. Finally, special thanks to Nigel Ede for asking me to do this book and for his enthusiasm, encouragement, phone calls and trust in letting me loose on a project like this.

Foreword

I started writing poetry when I was fifteen. It wasn't until I had turned thirty-eight that a Dragonfly landed on my shirt and virtually commanded me to look at it. I was stunned by it's beauty. So began a journey that eventually led me to give up my London job and set up the National Dragonfly Museum. The journey led me through many hours beside glittering, sunlit water, when the sight of a Dragonfly flashing past would instantly fill me with joy.

This book highlights that delight of watching Dragonflies. Although it is filled with facts, it is immediately accessible to beginners. It is the sort of book which sends you out to your local pond or river to see what is there and to learn. It's colourful, sketchbook style shows that identifying Dragonflies is usually relatively easy and is always fun. Dan Powell's paintings capture the spirit of each species. Whilst remaining free of sentiment, they have clearly been painted with love.

Museum volunteers will confirm that there is something magical about an insect which can elicit involuntary shouts of glee, not only from children but also from the most staid of adults. These are moments of pure joy and this book is about helping people towards such moments.

In fifteen years of Dragonflies I have only managed one poem about them. Here it is:

My Dragonflies

Of all the insects in the skies
The brightest are my dragonflies
My dragonflies are stained-glass men
Who loop and turn and loop again
On crystal wings they catch the light
Like neon shards in jump-jet flight

The sun and wind combine to make
A million diamonds on my lake,
Ripple-flash echoes on my mill
My dragonflies are brighter still.

Ashton Mill 1996

Ruary Mackenzie Dodds, Chairman, Board of Trustees of The National Dragonfly Museum.

♂ - danae

Introduction

What is it about this group of insects that continually fascinates us? Not just their superb flight as they hunt across pools and glades, performing extraordinary aerobatics, or even the beauty of their myriad of colours. Perhaps it has something to do with their mysterious, mostly aquatic life, which ends in a few short summer weeks as they fly in the sunlight to delight us. Whatever the reasons, they do have a hold on us, with which perhaps only the butterflies can compete.

This fascination has led writers and poets to be inspired by Dragonflies. In a few lines from "The Lady of Shalott" Tennyson captured both their beauty and essence.

> "Today I saw the dragonfly
> come from the wells where he did lie.
> An inner impulse rent the veil
> of his old husk; from head to tail
> came out clear plates of sapphire mail.
> He dried his wings: like gauze they grew;
> thro' crofts and pastures wet with dew
> a living flash of light he flew".

In 1937 H. E. Bates wrote of Dragonflies in 'Down the River'.

"It was a continuous turning and returning, an endless darting, poising, striking and hovering, so swift that it was often lost in sunlight".

No 'Horse Stinger' or 'Hoss Adder' folklore contained in these lines, just simple and accurate first-hand observations. The literary connection does not end there. Rumour has it even Winnie the Pooh was caught watching a hawker!

Wildlife, Dragonflies included, are there to be enjoyed, but most of us like to put a name to what it is we are looking at. The purpose of this guide is to enable you to identify the colourful blur that dashes by on a summer's day. All the Dragonflies present in this country are illustrated. The plates make up the bulk of this book, presenting them as living species, depicted as you will see them in the field, not as museum specimens. They will show you something of their habits and their "jizz", which are useful pointers to identification, especially if only brief views are obtained.

The first part of this book will give you a broad base of knowledge, information that will hopefully fire your interest in Dragonflies. Identification of the small number of species found in Britain will encourage further study; be it scientific or aesthetic, it will certainly never be dull. It is important to know something of their anatomy, life cycle and the habitats in which they are found, as well as their conservation, the practicalities of fieldcraft and getting to grips with the species. All these aspects are covered.

You will have to travel the country widely to see all the species, with visits to Southern England, Norfolk, the far north of Scotland and a trip to Ireland, essential. Given a year or two, a little determination and fair weather, all can be seen, some set against a backdrop of the most beautiful scenery you can imagine.

We hope that from May to September, the months will take on a new meaning through the absorbing pastime of Dragonfly watching.

What are they?

Two hundred and fifty million years ago the first true Dragonflies lived on earth. Fossil evidence shows that fifty million years earlier a primitive ancestor with a wingspan of 70 centimetres was flying.

Today around 5,300 species are on the wing, approximately half damselflies and half dragonflies. Most prefer to live in the warmth of the tropics, but some have adapted to cooler lands, with about 120 species found in Europe, of which 38 regularly breed in Britain.

A FOSSIL DRAGONFLY
Prehistoric Dragonflies
had to avoid predators
such as Pterosaurs,
the ancient equivalent
of a Hobby.

Dragonflies belong to the insect order known as Odonata, which relates to serrations on the mouthparts and means quite literally "toothed jaw". The order is divided into three suborders, species from two of which appear in Britain and Ireland. These are Zygoptera – the damselflies, and Anisoptera – the dragonflies. The term Dragonfly, with a capital "D", is used throughout the book to describe both groups together.

Anatomy

Adult bodies are made up of three sections head, thorax and abdomen. The differences between the adult forms of damsel and dragonflies, are straightforward. Damselflies are tiny, dainty fliers, looking like multi-coloured matchsticks with a helicopter's manoeuvrability. The rectangular-shaped head has eyes positioned on each end. The wings are attached to the thorax, which is the powerhouse of the body. When at rest, the wings are held closed along the line of the abdomen. This contrasts with the dragonflies, whose wings are held open at right-angles to the thorax.

Apart from the way the wings are held, dragonflies differ by being larger, more striking looking insects, with a dramatic forceful flight. The head is a half sphere containing mouthparts and a large pair of eyes. The abdomen is more varied in shape, with the hawker types being long, slim "panatella" shaped and vividly coloured, compared with the chasers and darters which are shorter, more robust and generally pastel shaded.

Zygoptera – damselflies

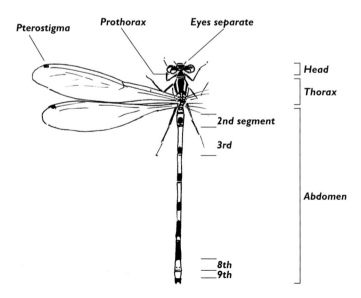

Anisoptera – dragonflies

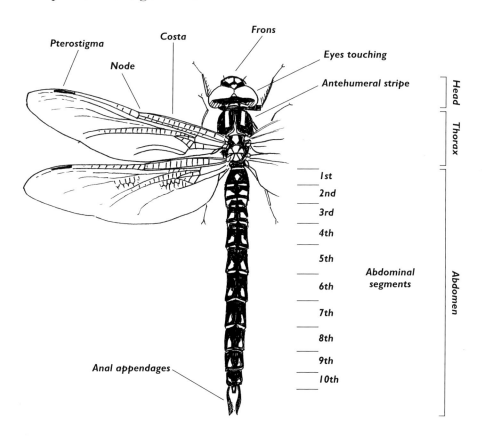

Pterostigma

Node

Costa

Frons

Eyes touching

Antehumeral stripe

Head

Thorax

1st
2nd
3rd
4th
5th
6th
7th
8th
9th
10th

Abdominal segments

Abdomen

Anal appendages

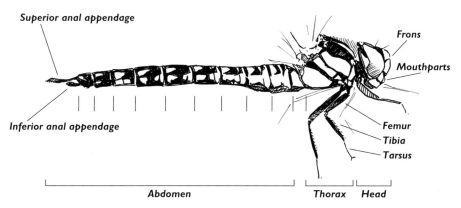

Superior anal appendage

Frons

Mouthparts

Inferior anal appendage

Femur
Tibia
Tarsus

Abdomen

Thorax

Head

Life cycle & behaviour

While tackling the problems of identification of Dragonflies, observing their unique life cycle and behaviour can have added rewards. It will reveal a remarkable transformation from a water dwelling larvae to an aerial life as an adult, which are the two distinct stages of life.

It takes a few days, longer if the weather is cool, for a Dragonfly to mature. This time is spent away from the water, to avoid being caught up in the skirmishing of mature males. Woods and hedgerows are favoured, and at this teneral and maturing stage, they can prove easier to study and photogragh. When they mature, they move to the water and take part in battles for a territory. If all the available territories are taken up, they try their luck at finding females in the surrounding area, where life is a little less frantic.

A WOODLAND POND SHOWING THE AREAS USED BY BROAD-BODIED CHASERS

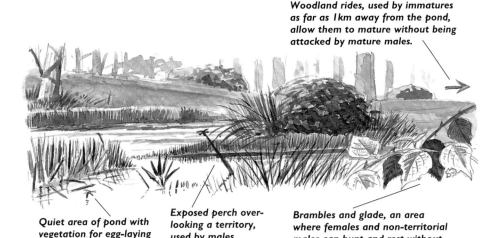

Woodland rides, used by immatures as far as 1km away from the pond, allow them to mature without being attacked by mature males.

Quiet area of pond with vegetation for egg-laying and emergence of larva.

Exposed perch over-looking a territory, used by males.

Brambles and glade, an area where females and non-territorial males can hunt and rest without being hassled by territorial males.

Dragonflies are carnivores, eating anything from midges to butterflies and even damselflies by the larger species. They eat up to one fifth of their body weight each day. Their large compound eyes are extremely sensitive to colour and movement, giving them a tremendous edge when being hunter or hunted. Hunting is usually the first activity of a Dragonfly's day. They fly with their legs held forward, the leg spines forming a basket, which effectively trawl the air, in order to catch their prey.

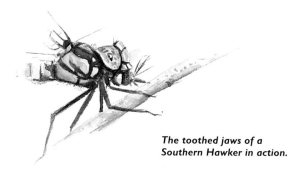

*The toothed jaws of a
Southern Hawker in action.*

The next activity after a good meal is to find a mate. Before arriving at the pond prior to mating, the male dragonfly transfers his sperm from the genital opening on the ninth segment of his abdomen, into the accessory genitalia on the second and third segments. Damselflies do this after a mate has been clasped. When a mate is found, he grasps her thorax with his legs. He will then attempt to place the claspers at the end of his abdomen, onto the prothorax which is behind the head of damselflies or on to the back of the eyes of dragonflies. If the female is willing the attempt will be successful, allowing the male to free his legs, thus enabling the pair to fly off in tandem. She then curls her abdomen around to form a wheel position, with her genital opening pushed against the accessory genitalia of the male.

*Damselflies (left) and dragonflies
(right) forming the wheel or heart.*

Certain male Dragonflies then indulge in some extraordinary behaviour. The male removes the sperm from the female, that has been placed there by previous mating, before introducing his own. This is acheived by one of two methods, either by, simply scraping the sperm out with his genitalia, or by the shape of his genitalia forcing the sperm out on entry. This is an example of sperm competition taken to extremes. Other insect species perform this, but not to the same extent. The length of time over which copulation takes place varies, but can last from several frantic seconds in flight for Broad-bodied Chaser, to a sedate perched courtship of a few hours for Common Hawker.

The claspers work by gripping behind the eyes of dragonflies (left) or onto the prothorax of damselflies (right). Their unique shape ensures that the claspers do not fit onto females of other species. Some fired up males may attempt to mate with other female species if they appear on his territory, though with little success.

Depending on the species, females lay their eggs directly by means of an ovipositor into mud and vegetation like Southern Hawker, or place them while in flight, by dipping the abdomen into the water so the eggs are washed off, like Brilliant Emerald. Damelflies and darters often maintain the tandem position while the female is ovipositing. Some male chasers, like Broad-bodied, escort the female as she egg-lays, chasing off intruding rivals. The hawkers are solitary and secretive in their egg-laying activity.

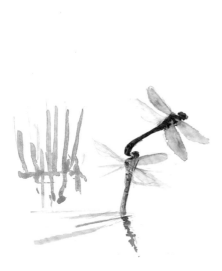

(above)
Detail of a Common Blue Damselfly inserting eggs into a plant stem.

(left) Ruddy Darters egg-laying in tandem.

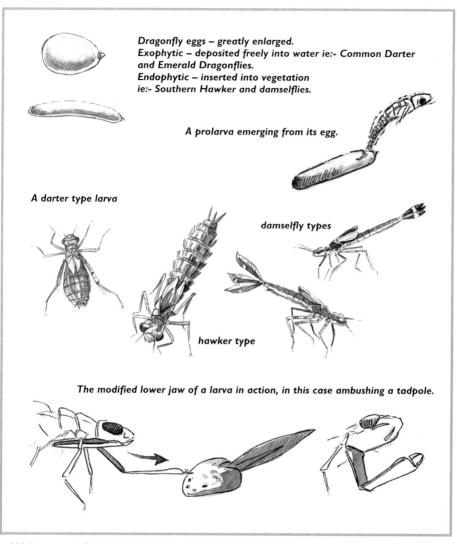

Dragonfly eggs – greatly enlarged.
Exophytic – deposited freely into water ie:- Common Darter and Emerald Dragonflies.
Endophytic – inserted into vegetation ie:- Southern Hawker and damselflies.

A prolarva emerging from its egg.

A darter type larva

damselfly types

hawker type

The modified lower jaw of a larva in action, in this case ambushing a tadpole.

Within twenty-four hours the eggs will change from cream to brown in colour. With some species, such as Azure Hawker, the eggs remain dormant and pass through the winter in a diapause state – a resting stage in the life cycle. Others will hatch in up to five weeks, the prolarva then emerging from the egg. Soon, usually within a few hours, the prolarva's skin is shed and the larva develops. As it matures the larva moults its skin up to 15 times during its aquatic life.

The larva is a voracious killer, taking anything smaller than itself and sometimes larger prey, even small fish. The mouthparts have a modified hinged lower jaw which can be thrust forward rapidly like a spear, helping to catch prey easily. Some species hunt among aquatic vegetation, while others remain concealed in the mud waiting for something tasty to swim by.

It usually takes one or two years before the adults emerge. Some hawkers may take three, with Golden-ringed Dragonfly taking up to five years or more, those living further north taking longer owing to the cold temperature of the water. Spring-flying species such as Club-tailed Dragonfly usually emerge en masse, temperature and day-length being the controlling factors. This synchronised emergence, does not occur with summer-flying species which emerge later in the year.

Emerging damselfly, chaser and hawker.

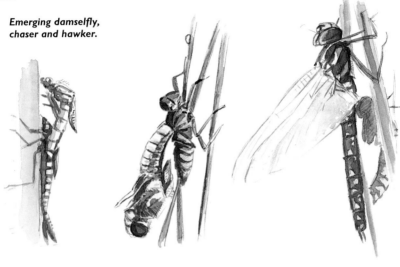

A teneral Common Darter drying off.

When the time for metamorphosis is at hand the larva climb a plant stem or crawl out onto a bank, usually in darkness. When dry, the thorax will start to split and the Dragonfly will slowly appear, now air-breathing not gill breathing as it was as a larva. Drying-off for the newly emerged Dragonfly, or teneral as it is known, can take up to three hours. Both body and wings are soft, making them vulnerable to predation by spiders and birds, many are lost at this stage. If any vegetation obstructs the expansion the wings, deformities can occur, preventing their maiden flight. The many Dragonflies that do make it are an amazing sight as they flutter off on unsteady shiny wings. For some their first flight is an even more impressive feat. They make a slow take-off to hundreds of feet and, if avian predators are avoided, they can drift for miles on air currents, resulting in a widespread dispersal. This behaviour is crucial to species that rely on static bodies of water for their existence, as ponds and ditches are continually lost, due to drying out or filling in, so new sites need to be continually sought out.

Broad-bodied Chaser with deformed wings, the insect is perfectly healthy apart from this, but it's inability to fly means it cannot feed, so is destined to a brief existence.

Their long life under water is contrasted with their short life as an adult. Damselflies live on average up to two weeks, certainly no longer than eight, and dragonflies live up to three weeks, with six weeks being exceptional. Short though their adult life is, it is an amazing and eventful one, giving us as observers of it, tremendous pleasure.

Starting out

One of the pleasures of watching Dragonflies is that it is best done in sunny weather. To visit a suitable habitat on a dull day can be tremendously disappointing, as it is usually totally devoid of activity. Visit the same place on a sunny day and the scene is transformed by a mass of activity. So this is the first rule of Dragonfly watching. Go when the sun shines.

The next rule is the time of the year you look for a species. A bluish dragonfly seen in late May will not be a Migrant Hawker, which flies late in the season, from early August to late autumn, but is more likely to be a Hairy Dragonfly, an early flyer, on the wing from early May to mid June. Therefore, knowing the flying period of a Dragonfly is often a very critical factor.

Use the maps to compare the distribution trends of similar species, in this case Blue-tailed Damselfly (left) and Scarce Blue-tailed Damselfly (right).

What species occur in which area? If you live in Birmingham, Northern Damselfly will not be on your local patch, as it only occurs in Scotland, nor will a brown dragonfly be Norfolk Hawker, as it is found only in East Anglia.

These three factors, the weather, flying period and distribution, are the bedrock of successful Dragonfly watching. When only limited views of a Dragonfly are obtained a process of elimination, using flying period and distribution will quickly reduce your options as to what it is you are watching.

Information sources

Part of the fun with learning about a new group of beasts is "genning up" and making plans for your approach to seeing the different species. The following are a few suggested sources of useful information.

Butterflies and Dragonflies A Site Guide – Paul Hill & Colin Twist, published by Arlequin Press, is an indispensable companion to this guide. It names the sites you will need to visit to see all the species of both groups of insects. Note that all the figures in brackets found throughout this field guide refer to the number of the site in the other guide.

The Atlas of the Dragonflies of Britain and Ireland published by the HMSO, is a very detailed and useful guide to the areas of Britain where each species may be found.

The British Dragonfly Society, among its many activities, organises fieldtrips with the aim of seeing a wide range of the Dragonflies in all parts of the country. These trips are listed in the twice-yearly newsletter members receive, along with a more scientifically based journal, catering for many needs.

On a more local level, helpful contacts could be your county wildlife trust, natural history society or the wildlife section of the nearest museum.

Finding your own Dragonfly site

The identification of an ideal habitat for Dragonflies is almost instinctive, but a number of hints can help you to spot one. As stated before, Dragonflies rely on water to play out most of their lives, so, to stand the best chance of seeing the greatest number of species, a visit to a wetland site is essential. The most favoured types are ponds, gravel pits, canals, rivers and acid bogs.

With a local map in hand, pick out and explore a body of fresh water, a pond for example. Ponds are a good place to start because they are plentiful, widespread and support many of the common species.

First, check that the water is clear, not covered in duckweed or containing large amounts of algae. On closer inspection, if various pondweeds and other healthy emergent vegetation on the margins are growing, the signs are looking very optimistic. Add to this, shrubs and trees nearby which give shelter, but are not so close as to pollute the water with their fallen leaves, plus an area of grassland containing a variety of plants where species can hunt, completes the recipe to what must be a really good potential Dragonfly habitat. Of course, if it is swarming with the beasts, you know you are onto a winner!

When you have found such a habitat, you may discover that it benefits other kinds of wildlife, such as birds, mammals, butterflies or other insects. It is then a fine example of bio-diversity. Indeed, the presence of Dragonflies is often used as an indicator of sustainability (the ability of a system to survive into the future), as most can only live in a clean environment.

When visiting any habitat it is crucial to make the least impact on it. Excessive trampling of wetland vegetation causes great damage, especially to fragile sphagnum bogs. More will be seen by sitting and waiting, than by bashing about, as with any wildlife watching.

What species to look for first

Don't be daunted by the similarity of certain species; there are not too many of them to remember, unlike birds. Once you begin to separate them into damselflies and dragonflies, eliminate those that do not occur in that area and start to recognise the main features, they suddenly become more manageable.

Damselflies are probably the easier group to start with, owing to their more sedentary nature. They even fly in dull and rainy weather. In inclement conditions they seek shelter, gathering in areas of grassland or rushes. Annoyingly, they can perch on the far side of the stems, and will even move around them to avoid the observer.

One defence system of damselflies is to hide behind a plant putting a stem between themselves and a would-be predator, while maintaining a watchful eye on the danger.

As you become used to various habitats, you will be aware that certain species are almost guaranteed to be present. Blue-tailed Damselfly is one, it is the most pollution tolerant, which helps to make it widespread and more likely to be encountered. Other damselflies commonly found in a variety of habitats include Azure, Common Blue, Large Red and Emerald. Make yourself familiar with the main identification features of these to start with, it will help you immensely when you come across the rarer damselflies.

WHAT TO LOOK OUT FOR FIRST
When you start to look at damselflies take note of their different attitudes at rest.
Demoiselles will often perch with a perky stance, abdomen lifted.
Emeralds perch with wings held partly open.
Other damselflies hold their wings along the abdomen.

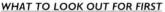

When identifying the male blue damselflies practise your field craft by getting close up to them and studying the segment markings especially segments two, eight and nine.

Damselflies are fairly weak fliers, so tend not to be far from water. This is not true of the dragonflies. The common species, when not defending a territory on your ideal wetland habitat, may be found feeding or gaining warmth along forest rides and hedgerows, in parks, gardens and other similar areas; indeed anywhere that is quiet and sunny. The ones to look out for are Migrant, Southern and Brown Hawkers, Emperor Dragonfly and Ruddy, Common and Highland Darters, depending on where you are.

Look at the profiles of dragonflies in flight and you will begin to notice subtle differences between Emeralds (left) small and neat, Emperor (middle) large slightly bowed and Hawkers (right) large slightly upturned.

You may also find that if one species is present in a particular habitat, you will start to associate it with a number of others and expect to see them. At your pond (in the south), if Broad-bodied Chaser is apparent, then check the edges for the common damselflies as listed earlier. There may be a patrolling Southern Hawker and an imperious Emperor on the wing. Where floating vegetation such as Water-lilies are present look out for Red-eyed Damselfly, a less common species. They like to sit out in the open on water plants for lengthy periods, so are not easily overlooked.

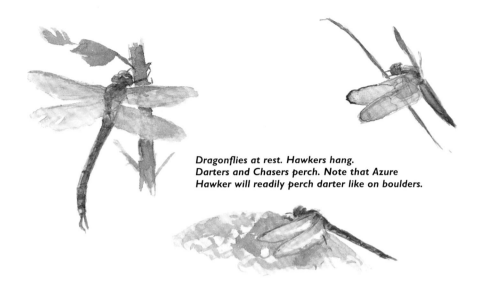

*Dragonflies at rest. Hawkers hang.
Darters and Chasers perch. Note that Azure
Hawker will readily perch darter like on boulders.*

Many common species are widespread across a number of habitats, but some rarer ones are restricted to particular habitats, Small Red Damselfly and White-faced Darter rely on more acid areas. When on fenland sites check carefully through the Azures for Variable Damselfly and the Emeralds for Scarce Emerald, the habitat favoured by these species. It is hard to understand why species like Variable are relatively rare while Azure, which is superficially similar, so abundant. Such is the mystery of Dragonfly watching, but with greater coverage, study and understanding, their needs may be identified and suitable habitats created for them.

The habitats

With interest in Dragonflies spreading, it is not surprising that many excellent and important habitats have already been identified. This section describes the key ones, the likely Dragonflies to be found at them and a typical location. Habitats can be broken down into two main types, static water bodies and flowing water.

Static water bodies

This term covers a whole multitude of habitats, from village and farm ponds, to ditches, lakes, gravel pits and acid bogs. It is at these sites where the numbers and diversity of Dragonfly species are at their best.

WHERE TO LOOK FOR SPECIES AT A POND

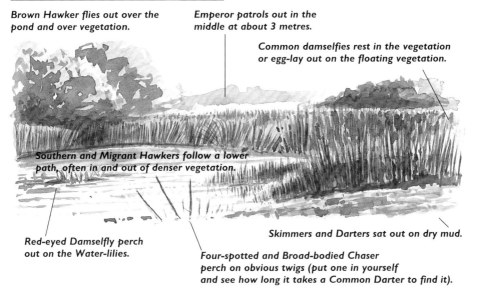

Brown Hawker flies out over the pond and over vegetation.

Emperor patrols out in the middle at about 3 metres.

Common damselfies rest in the vegetation or egg-lay out on the floating vegetation.

Southern and Migrant Hawkers follow a lower path, often in and out of denser vegetation.

Red-eyed Damselfly perch out on the Water-lilies.

Four-spotted and Broad-bodied Chaser perch on obvious twigs (put one in yourself and see how long it takes a Common Darter to find it).

Skimmers and Darters sat out on dry mud.

Ponds

At a lowland pond, in the south, dashing out from perches on the perimeter vegetation, will be Four-spotted and Broad-bodied Chaser, the thugs of the pool. Also active, often from the baked mud of a bank, will fly Black-tailed Skimmer, or later on in the year the fidgety Common and Ruddy Darters.

Brown Hawker with their orange, gauzy wings, prefer to hawk out over open water, with Southern Hawker more confined to the edges. With a little experience, features such as the blue bow-shaped abdomen of the Emperor Dragonfly will stand out from the straighter bodies of the other hawkers, as it patrols the pond.

A typical habitat for some of these can be found at Vale Royal Locks in Cheshire (107). Here a variety of species occur at a pond managed by fishermen. These include Hairy Dragonfly, Four-spotted Chaser and all the common species of damselfly. The vegetation is very lush and the site sheltered by mature trees. There is a good cross-section of birds and butterflies, plus other insect activity.

Kingsbury Water Park in Warwickshire (54), is a good example of an old gravel pit, that is now being managed for wildlife.

On the lowland floodplains of East Anglia and Southern England, another set of species can be seen. Ditches and dykes in these areas can provide the right circumstances for Variable and Emerald Damselflies, Hairy Dragonfly and in East Anglia only, Norfolk Hawker and Scarce Emerald Damselfly. Norfolk Hawker particularly like dykes with a high water level on grazing marshes where the plant Water Soldier is present. Upton Fen in Norfolk (106) is a good site with open fen, dykes woodland and pools. There is a waymarked trail taking you through these habitats. It is an important reserve for Dragonflies and Fenland Plants such as Marsh Helleborine and Fen Orchid. Check the open grassy area as you enter the reserve for Norfolk Hawker. Scarce Emerald Damselfly has similar requirements, but is also seen on pingos, ponds unique to Breckland.

AN ACID POND

Emperor fly high out over the middle.

Common Hawker creep around the edges or perch high in conifers.

Downy and Brilliant Emeralds along tree-lined edges

White-faced Darter sit on the sphagnum moss or typically on white dead wood.

Adjacent vegetation, Black Darter, Large and Small Red Damselfly.

Four-spotted Chaser on obvious perches.

At more acidic heathland ponds and bogs, other Dragonflies thrive. Common Hawker creep along the edges of pools, but is not all that common in the south! Keeled Skimmer and Black

Darter, can be very abundant at their best locations, with Keeled scrapping with all sizes of Dragonflies if they encroach onto their territory. Black Darter has similar restless habits, often returning to the same perch when disturbed. The rare White-faced Darter is relatively easy to identify, but has a very limited distribution. It seems to particularly like perching on pale dead wood and areas of sphagnum moss.

Emerald Dragonflies are slightly larger than the darters. When patrolling an area of pond, their metallic green bodies gleam, and they frequently skirmish with the more robust chasers that infringe on their patches. None of them are very common. Northern Emerald prefers acidic pools, Downy and Brilliant tolerate both mildly alkaline and acidic waters.

SCOTTISH BOG

Resting in glades Common Hawker, Golden-ringed Dragonfly (if there is a stream nearby), Northern Emerald, plus many of the others.

Northern Emerald hunting at about 3 metres around the trees or at about a metre over the pools.

Among the pools Common Hawker, Four-spotted Chaser, Highland, White-faced and Black Darters, Emerald and Large Red Damselfly.

Azure Hawker, resting on boulders or on tree trunks and out over the bog.

Bridge of Grudie by Loch Maree in Scotland (21) is a superb example of a boggy habitat. It consists of a very open area of small shallow bog pools, with a tree-lined stream on one side that forms glades which provide loafing spots for the Dragonflies. On a hot summer's day you will need to separate Common from Azure Hawker, with the Common's yellow forewing (or costa) and the tendency of Azure Hawker to perch on boulders, being great aids with this task. Other northern specialities can be found here; Northern Emerald, Highland Darter, and White-faced Darter fly among the more common Large Red and Emerald Damselflies, Four-spotted Chaser, Black Darter and Golden-ringed Dragonfly. Other kinds of wildlife to look out for include Large Heath Butterfly, plenty of blood-sucking insects, and a number of birds including Golden Eagle, Buzzard and Black-throated Diver. Orchids such as Creeping Lady's Tresses can also be found, all against a fantastic and unspoilt backdrop of loch and mountains.

Many of the species which occur commonly on lowland pools, canals and other water bodies are also found in acidic habitats. For example Common Blue Damselfly is often alongside Northern Damselfly in Scotland, creating identification problems. Four-spotted Chaser can often be found flying with the Emeralds, causing confusion when in flight, though not at rest.

HIGHLAND LOCH

Common Hawker patrolling the ponds' edge.

Black Darter, Northern, Common Blue, Large Red and Emerald Damselfly on vegetation around the edge.

White-faced Darter sat on sphagnum moss or white dead wood. If disturbed they can disappear up into neighbouring trees.

Finally, Irish Damselfly is found on slightly alkaline lakes with moderate levels of dissolved nutrients and also in mildly acidic small peaty pools with similar nutrients present. These are the preferred conditions in Ireland. It, as yet, has not been discovered on similar patches this side of the Irish Sea, so if you like a challenge . . .

Flowing water

Moderate and Fast Flowing

At a fast flowing river or stream you are unlikely to come across many Dragonflies, the hard bottom and lack of aquatic vegetation on this type of river present unfavourable conditions for larvae to develop. However, on slightly slower rivers, the situation is different. The dynamic Golden-ringed Dragonfly patrols deep cut, small heathland streams. If the stream is dapple shaded and shallow, with a shingle bottom, then you may be lucky to witness the exotic Beautiful Demoiselle performing their dancing display. On unshaded patches of the stream the diminutive Southern Damselfly could be present. One location to see it in abundance is Brynberian in Dyfed (25).

Crockford Bridge in the New Forest (49) is a well known Dragonfly site, with an impressive number of species. On a short stretch of stream, Southern, Small Red, and Large Red Damselfly can be closely scrutinised, with Beautiful Demoiselle, Golden-ringed Dragonfly and Keeled Skimmer making a very varied selection. Check for Purple Hairstreak Butterflies around the car park and be sure to scan the surrounding open heath. Some of the Hobbies hunting there in the spring of '98 turned out to be Red-footed Falcons!

Patrolling low along the stream
Golden-ringed Dragonfly.

Perched on over-hanging plants
Beautiful Demoiselle.

On perches or exposed dry
mud *Keeled Skimmer.*

Tucked into vegetation *Southern,*
Small Red and *Large Red Damselfly.*

Out on the Heather female
Southern Damselfly, Keeled
Skimmer and *Black Darter.*

Slow flowing

Lowland river systems and canals come into this category. There are prizes to be discovered watching slow rivers and Club-tailed Dragonfly is one. Mainly restricted to a few large river systems in southern Britain, with silt or mud bottoms, they spend a considerable amount of time in woodland areas, even up to 16 kilometres away from the breeding site. When searching for Club-tailed on the river, you are likely to come across Banded Demoiselle and White-legged Damselfly, frequently in large numbers.

SLOWER LARGE RIVERS

Emerging Club-tailed Dragonflies rest
and harden-off in riverside vegetation
such as nettles and comfrey.
Females egg-lay out in the middle of the river.

Check the riverside plants also
for Banded Demoiselle, White-legged Damselfly,
plus common damselflies and Scarce Chaser.

Scarce Chaser is the other gem. It has a decidedly limited distribution, preferring sluggish flowing rivers and dykes, with wooded patches close by, for feeding and shelter. A trip to New Bridge in West Sussex (74), on the old Wey & Arun Canal and the River Arun itself, during early June should give you chance to see a good selection of lowland river species, such as White-legged Damselfly, Hairy Dragonfly, Downy Emerald, Club-tailed Dragonfly and Scarce Chaser.

Atcham on the River Severn in Shropshire (7) is another good example of a slow-flowing river; it has White-legged Damselfly, Club-tailed Dragonfly and Banded Demoiselle along its banks.

Scarce Blue-tailed Damselfly tolerates both acid and alkaline waters and is found along slow-flowing seepages, streams and runnels which are mineral enriched. Where spring lines in industrial workings such as quarries are present, the species is also worth seeking out. Mill Lawn Brook in Hampshire (68) is where many try for this damselfly, along with Southern Damselfly and Keeled Skimmer.

SEEPAGE

Broad-bodied Chaser roaring about everywhere.
Common Darter around the edges.

Tucked into the vegetation Scarce Blue-tailed Damselfly. They sometimes seek shelter in adjacent vegetation.

Also look for Blue-tailed Damselfly for comparison. Southern Damselfly may be present.

To choose a site that is as good for Dragonflies as Minsmere is for birds is not a difficult one. Supporting 26 breeding species Thursley Common in Surrey (103), must surely be one of the finest. A combination of ponds, bog and stream hold a mouth-watering selection, where Small Red and Red-eyed Damselfly, Downy and Brilliant Emeralds, Golden-ringed, Common and Brown Hawkers, Keeled Skimmer, Black Darter and Beautiful Demoiselle are the pick. As with any superb habitat other wildlife abounds. Hobbies make for ambivalent viewing as they make dents in the Dragonfly population and look out also for Tree Pipit and Dartford Warbler. A large population of Silver-studded Blue and Grayling Butterflies add to what can make a memorable visit to this site.

Rare migrants

In the last three years Red-veined Darter has established breeding colonies in Southern Britain. One of these is as far north as Spurn on Humberside, where the colony has been established since 1996.

With the expansion northwards of resident species such as Black-tailed Skimmer, Ruddy Darter and Emperor in the last decade, it is quite possible that species present in the near continent may soon form breeding colonies in Britain.

Finally, news may come of an invasion, as in 1995 when Yellow-winged Darters arrived from the continent. At least eight vagrant species have been seen in Britain and a "twitch" to see a new one starts the adrenalin flowing. You never know where they are going to turn up, some avoid water altogether. It may be you who finds the next new species for Britain. While this book was in the making, several Green Darners made the incredible journey across the Atlantic to join the British List.

Field-craft

So you have identified a good habitat. It is a sunny, summer's day. What is the best time to start searching for them?

Well, 9am will do. At that hour a typical day will be a little cool and the Dragonflies still dozy. This means that when disturbed they may not fly far, but land close by, hopefully in a position where they can be closely examined.

Late morning is a busy time for Dragonflies and can be the most productive period for watching their behaviour. On very hot days, the activities can cease in the afternoon as species need to rest up, to avoid over-heating. As the day cools, things naturally quieten down and you might just be lucky to catch sight of an Emperor as it settles in to roost, right by your side.

Nothing is more aggravating than going along a pond edge and flushing a species which immediately flies off into the distance. This will happen a lot! However, if the Dragonfly settles back in view, this is the time to be patient and stealthy.

On first approach the best policy is to watch it using your binoculars. Then by slowly moving, not rushing in, you should be rewarded with superb prolonged naked eye views. Keep your movements to a minimum and you might even find yourself the territorial perch of a Ruddy Darter! If the sun goes in after they alight, so much the better, as their tendency to fly off is reduced and your study can be leisurely.

After some time you will sense when a Dragonfly wants to rest. This is especially true of the hawkers. Their movements seem to become secretive, deliberate and confined to a particular area. They often make several "trial" landings before selecting a perch, affording a great chance to study and photograph them. Mind you, they often land out of reach, halfway up a tree!.

Equipment

Your clothing will help with successful observation, dull coloured material is best. Wellies are essential, though perhaps uncomfortable after a short while on a hot day. Always wear a hat with a brim to avoid too much sun, but most important of all take along a bucket load of blood sucker insect repellent. It pays to look trendy in a bog!

Binoculars are an invaluable aid. A close-focusing pair down to 2 metres, with a wide field of view, for following species in flight, is very useful. These can be expensive, so it is worth considering a second-hand pair. Ziess Jenoptem 8 x 30 were a good pair reasonably priced when new, but are now gold-dust since being withdrawn. A telescope can occasionally be useful, especially when insects are perched high in trees or in the middle of a sphagnum bog. To help you make your choice, it is worth reading the optics reviews that often appear in the birding press.

Note-taking is a real help in refining your skills. Make them while you are watching the species, not later. It is surprising how quickly you can forget what you have seen. Do not be afraid of writing on identification guides (even this one!). If a particular feature stands out, make a note of it. The definitive guide has yet to be written, so your notes could be important. Details of

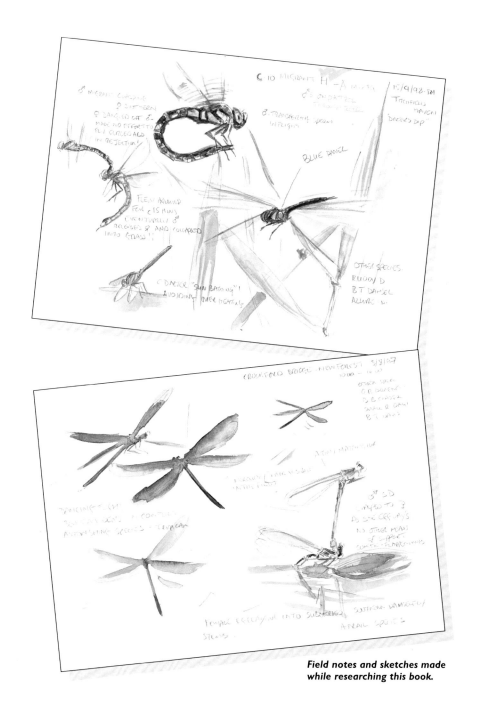

Field notes and sketches made while researching this book.

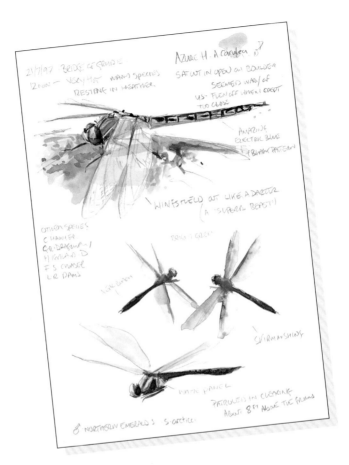

numbers, age, sex etc, are all worth keeping and passing on to the local recorder, along with habitat details and location. Proof of breeding is invaluable, so keep records of mating, egg-laying and any finds or counts of larvae and exuviae.

For photographers the need to be near your quarry is paramount. When approaching a species, the last step always seems to cause the problem. You put your weight onto the most comfortable leg, balance yourself, take a deep breath lean over and ..... damn its flown. Try again, this time take care not to kick the bush or throw your shadow over it as you go in. Good luck!

In gathering the reference material needed to produce this book, the aid of a decent pair of bins, a camera, good fieldcraft, a notebook and incredible luck with the weather were the ingredients for success. One piece of equipment that was intentionally not used was a net. Firstly to prove that Dragonflies can be identified purely by fieldcraft, which they were, and secondly a net is a right pain to keep carrying around.

It is impossible to say why so much satisfaction can be gained from close encounters with humble species such as Dragonflies. The fact is, it can. Don't try to rationalise it or excuse it. Just do it. The more you do it the easier it becomes, but the pleasure never diminishes.

Conservation

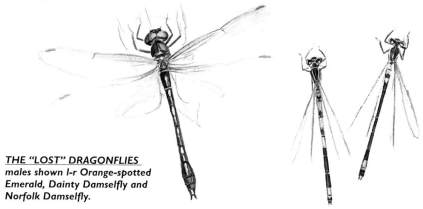

No home, no dragonfly

This is true of any creature, be they Dragonflies, Mammals, Birds or even Human beings. With Dragonfly conservation it is relatively simple, or perhaps simply difficult! They come to wetland habitats to breed. So, it is important that these habitats remain unpolluted and are managed in such a way as to encourage Dragonflies, which in turn will benefit other species too.

Today many habitats have been damaged or lost, the main culprits being industry and the change from traditional to industrial farming since the 1950's. With this change came the drainage and the use of chemicals on the land, this has proven particularly detrimental to most wildlife. Sometimes nature plays its own part. Encroachment by vegetation can dry out a wetland and a pool lined by trees can fill with leaves or shade out aquatic or marginal vegetation, rendering it unsuitable.

THE "LOST" DRAGONFLIES
males shown l-r Orange-spotted
Emerald, Dainty Damselfly and
Norfolk Damselfly.

Nature and man have been responsible for the loss of three species from this country within the last 50 years: Orange-spotted Emerald disappeared from the Moors River in Dorset as a result of pollution from a nearby housing estate; Dainty Damselfly was a victim of nature, when the sites in Essex were flooded by sea water and Norfolk Damselfly was lost due to its last remaining site being choked by vegetation. Although these Dragonflies were on the edge of their range, let us hope that their fate will never be repeated. Not all is doom and gloom however. In fact, on the credit side Red-veined Darter and possibly Yellow-winged Darter, can now be regarded as residents, after several successful breeding seasons in this country, since their '95/96 invasion.

We have recognised the damaging effects of industrial pollution on many of our watercourses. Legislation, much of it EC inspired, has begun to contribute to a cleaner environment. Where communities have embraced the aspects of "Local Agenda 21" following the "Earth Summit" at Rio, the awareness of local involvement in environmental improvement grows.

A positive step to take at a local level, is to create a pond in your own garden, which will benefit Dragonflies. Nothing can be more attractive than a wildlife pond with your own Dragonflies to study and marvel at, but remember goldfish and larvae don't mix. A pond two metres by one and a half metres in a tiny garden had breeding Common Darter and Southern Hawker within three years of construction.

PROFILE OF A GARDEN POND

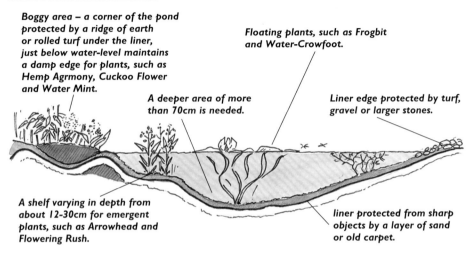

Boggy area – a corner of the pond protected by a ridge of earth or rolled turf under the liner, just below water-level maintains a damp edge for plants, such as Hemp Agrmony, Cuckoo Flower and Water Mint.

Floating plants, such as Frogbit and Water-Crowfoot.

A deeper area of more than 70cm is needed.

Liner edge protected by turf, gravel or larger stones.

A shelf varying in depth from about 12-30cm for emergent plants, such as Arrowhead and Flowering Rush.

liner protected from sharp objects by a layer of sand or old carpet.

POSITION wherever you like, but keep away from leaf-shedding plants that may choke the pond. Ideally it will have a sunny aspect. SIZE, as large or as small as your garden will allow. The larger it is then the more features you can build into it which makes it more attractive to wildlife. Remember Fish and Dragonflies do not mix well together.

Larger ponds do not have to be long-established to prove good for Dragonflies. One pond on the edge of a housing estate in industrial Merseyside, excavated about 20 years ago, 50 metres long by 20 metres wide, heavily fished by local youths and often full of litter, holds ten breeding species. The important factors are that it has aquatic vegetation, is unpolluted, has trees nearby, but not overhanging and has plenty of grassland, wildflowers and scrub adjacent which encourage a wide range of insects for prey and provides shelter.

It is good that Dragonfly conservation is now being taken seriously. Cornmill Dragonfly Sanctuary (29), part of the Lea Valley Park in North London, is a superb example. A mosaic of habitats provides a home for a large number of species and it is the premiere site in the region. The interpretation produced to describe the area is excellent, with all the species being found where the leaflet says they should be.

The National Dragonfly Museum near Oundle (73) is another exciting site promoting Dragonflies. There is a combination of indoor exhibits, including a live TV microscope link up and an outdoor Dragonfly trail, which all make for an informative visit. If public information is poor it is hardly likely that people will be inspired to be involved in the subject. Sites such as these are so important in promoting the cause of fragile groups like Dragonflies.

National wildlife organisations are now strongly concerned with Dragonfly conservation. The Royal Society for the Protection of Birds and the Wildfowl and Wetlands Trust both have large reserves and realise that their landholdings are important for all wildlife, not just birds.

The British Dragonfly Society, above all others, raises the awareness of the public to Dragonflies throughout the country. With newsletters, lectures, recording schemes and walks, they promote the cause of this small group of insects, which, when doing well reflect on the health of the environment as a whole. Your next move after reading this book should be to join this society.

Useful Contacts:
British Dragonfly Society – Secretary – The Haywain, Hollywater Rd, Borden, Hants GU35 0AD.
RSPB – The Lodge, Sandy, Beds SG19 2DL.
Wildfowl & Wetlands Trust – Slimbridge, Gloucestershire GL2 7BT.
The Wildlife Trusts – The Green, Witham Park, Waterside South, Lincoln LN5 7JR
Tel 01522 544400 for information about your local trust.

ABOUT THE PLATES

Virtually all the resident British species are given a double page showing males and females of varying ages and behaviour as they are seen in the field. Damselflies are scaled up half life-size and dragonflies a quarter. In the top left corner of each plate there is life-size silhouette of the species. "The status is a guide to distribution, not numbers of each species." The maps are there to show distribution trends not as detailed site guides. Remember also that the species concerned will generally only be found in the suitable habitat within the shown areas. The bracketed numbers refer to an ideal site in which to see the species, as described in THE SITE GUIDE BY COLIN TWIST AND PAUL HILL. This applies to the scarcer species only.

Quick reference guide

Damselflies

M & F. Wings coloured. Body metallic green or blue.

P 42 – Beautiful Demoiselle – Widespread
P 44 – Banded Demoiselle – Widespread

M & F. Wings clear. Body metallic green tinged orange.

P 46 – Emerald Damselfly – Very widespread
P 48 – Scarce Emerald Damselfly – Rare, East Anglia only

M & F. Abdomen red, some with black.

P 50 – Large Red Damselfly – Very widespread
P 52 – Small Red Damselfly – Scarce

**M & F. Abdomen patterned pale blue & black.
Legs white marked black *(similar to below)*.**

P 54 – White-legged Damselfly – Scarce

**M. Abdomen patterned blue & black.
F. Abdomen patterned green & black.**

P 56 – Common Blue Damselfly – Very widespread
P 58 – Azure Damselfly – Very widespread
P 60 – Variable Damselfly – Local
P 62 – Southern Damselfly – Rare
P 64 – Northern Damselfly – Very rare, Scotland only
P 66 – Irish Damselfly – Rare, Ireland only

M & F. Abdomen Black with blue or brown band near end.

P 68 – Blue-tailed Damselfly – Very widespread
P 70 – Scarce Blue-tailed Damselfly – Scarce
P 72 – Red-eyed Damselfly – Local

Flight period

APR	MAY	JUN	JUL	AUG	SEP	OCT

Habitat

RIVER	STREAM	ACID BOG	DITCH	CANAL	POND
○	●				
●	○			●	○
	○	●	●	●	●
			●		●
○	●	●	●	●	●
	●	○	●		
●	●			○	○
○	○	●	●	●	●
○	○	●	●	●	●
		○	●	○	●
	●				
			●		●
			○		●
○	○	●	●	●	●
	●				○
○				●	●

RIV	STR	ABOG	DIT	CAN	POND

Quick reference guide

Dragonflies

Larger dragonflies, including hawkers & emeralds.

M & F. Abdomen marked black & yellow.

P 74 – Club-tailed Dragonfly – Rare
P 76 – Golden-ringed Dragonfly – Widespread

M & F. Abdomen dark with pairs of blue, green or yellow spots.

P 78 – Hairy Dragonfly – Local
P 80 – Azure Hawker – Rare, Scotland only
P 82 – Southern Hawker – Very widespread
P 84 – Common Hawker – Very widespread
P 86 – Migrant Hawker – Widespread

M & F. Abdomen bright blue or green with dark line down centre *(similar to above group).*

P 88 – Emperor Dragonfly – Widespread

M & F. Abdomen brown.

P 90 – Norfolk Hawker – Very rare, Norfolk/Suffolk only
P 92 – Brown Hawker – Very widespread

M & F. Body metallic green with bronze sheen.

P 94 – Downy Emerald – Scarce
P 96 – Brilliant Emerald – Rare
P 98 – Northern Emerald – Rare, Scotland only

Flight period

APR	MAY	JUN	JUL	AUG	SEP	OCT

Habitat

RIVER	STREAM	ACID BOG	DITCH	CANAL	POND

APR	MAY	JUN	JUL	AUG	SEP	OCT

RIV	STR	ABOG	DIT	CAN	POND

Quick reference guide

Chasers, skimmers & darters.

M & F. Abdomen dull brown, wings with dark spots (*similar to below*).
P 100 – Four-spotted Chaser – Very widespread

M. Abdomen powder blue. F. Abdomen yellow, orange or brown, some with dark markings.
P 102 – Scarce Chaser – Rare
P 104 – Broad-bodied Chaser – Widespread
P 106 – Black-tailed Skimmer – Local
P 108 – Keeled Skimmer – Local

M. Abdomen red. F. Abdomen yellow or brown, with some dark markings.
P 110 – Common Darter – Very widespread
P 112 – Highland Darter – Scarce, Scotland only
P 114 – Ruddy Darter – Widespread

M. Mainly black with some yellow spots.
F. Mainly yellow with some black (*similar to above group*).
P 116 – Black Darter – Widespread

M & F. Abdomen black with red or cream spots. Face off white.
P 118 – White-faced Darter – Rare

Vagrants
P 120 – Yellow-winged Darter – Vagrant
P 121 – Red-veined Darter – Vagrant
P 122 – Vagrants I
P 124 – Vagrants II

Status – based on number of KM squares in which recorded. It is not an indicator of the quantity of each species within each square.
Very rare – 1-15
Rare – 16-100
Scarce – 101-250
Local – 251-450
Widespread – 451-880
Very widespread – 881-2200

⬤ Often seen in this habitat
◯ Sometimes seen in this habitat

Flight period

APR	MAY	JUN	JUL	AUG	SEP	OCT

Habitat

RIVER	STREAM	ACID BOG	DITCH	CANAL	POND

RIV	STR	ABOG	DIT	CAN	POND

Family CALOPTERYGIDAE

Beautiful Demoiselle
Calopteryx virgo

Similar species – Banded Demoiselle.
Jizz – Stunning, tropical, graceful.
Size – L-45mm, W male-58mm female-63mm
Flight period – End May – late August
Status – Widespread.
First impression – Large exotic damselfly. Delicate butterfly-like flight on dark wings, fluttering electric colours. Conspicuous. Both demoiselles are delightful, willingly accepting your presence in their world if you keep still, often using you as a perch.

Life size

Body metallic blue/green.

Eyes deep red.

MATURE MALE on Water Crowfoot.

MATURE FEMALE

Female wings – tinted pale golden brown, marked with a white false pterostigma. C.p. to pale green of Banded D.

Yellow marks on side of thorax and yellow line down centre of last three segments.

FEMALE – metallic green on head, thorax and abdomen, becoming bronze near tip.

OLD FEMALE – seen in Sept. N.b. much clearer wings.

Look for males along the streams perched on over-hanging branches and females on nearby bushes. Obvious in flight, like flickering coloured mirrors.

IMMATURE MALE at rest on Bog Myrtle. N.b. clear golden wings at this age. No pterostigma c.p. to female.

42

Male wings – almost black with flashes of iridescent blue/green, clearer at base. Wings broader and wing veins in both sexes more dense, c.p. to Banded D.

MALE
no pterostigma.

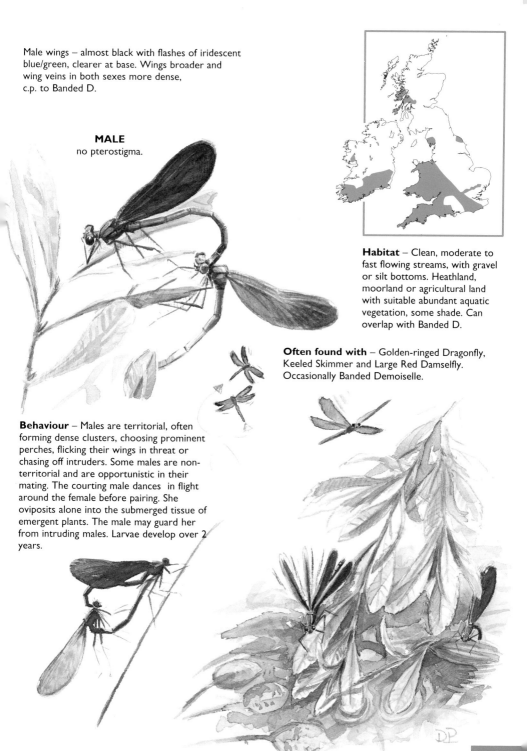

Habitat – Clean, moderate to fast flowing streams, with gravel or silt bottoms. Heathland, moorland or agricultural land with suitable abundant aquatic vegetation, some shade. Can overlap with Banded D.

Often found with – Golden-ringed Dragonfly, Keeled Skimmer and Large Red Damselfly. Occasionally Banded Demoiselle.

Behaviour – Males are territorial, often forming dense clusters, choosing prominent perches, flicking their wings in threat or chasing off intruders. Some males are non-territorial and are opportunistic in their mating. The courting male dances in flight around the female before pairing. She oviposits alone into the submerged tissue of emergent plants. The male may guard her from intruding males. Larvae develop over 2 years.

Family CALOPTERYGIDAE

Banded Demoiselle

Calopteryx splendens

Similar species – Beautiful Demoiselle.
Jizz – Exotic, beautiful, delicate.
Size – L-45mm, W-male- 61mm female-65mm
Flight period – May – September.
Status – Widespread.
First impression – Large unmistakable iridescent damselfly. Striking wing spots on males give them a flickering helicopter effect in flight.

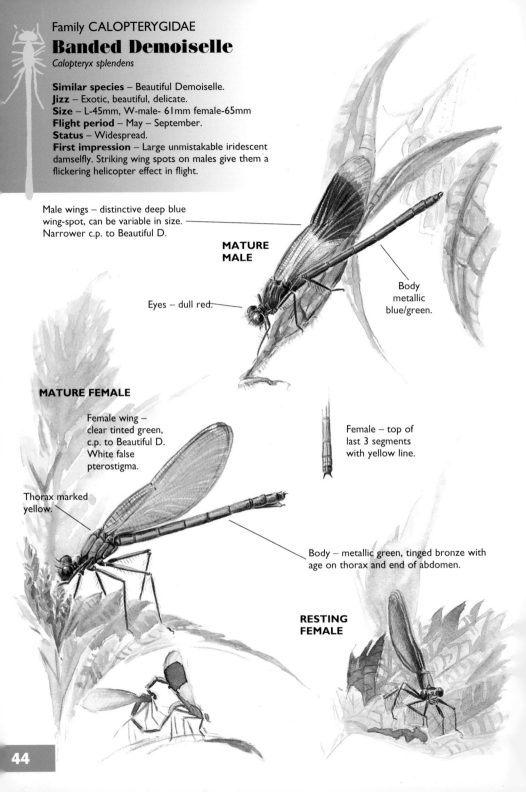

Male wings – distinctive deep blue wing-spot, can be variable in size. Narrower c.p. to Beautiful D.

MATURE MALE

Eyes – dull red.

Body metallic blue/green.

MATURE FEMALE

Female wing – clear tinted green, c.p. to Beautiful D. White false pterostigma.

Thorax marked yellow.

Female – top of last 3 segments with yellow line.

Body – metallic green, tinged bronze with age on thorax and end of abdomen.

RESTING FEMALE

Behaviour – Like Beautiful D. the males perform a fluttering display, before mating. The pair fly off in tandem to undisturbed surrounding vegetation, before the female returns alone to egg-lay into plant tissue above and below the water line. Larvae mature after 2 years.

Habitat – Unpolluted slow-moving muddy bottomed rivers or canals, rarely ponds. Abundant emergent vegetation present. Can overlap with Beautiful D.

Often found with – White-legged and Large Red Damselfly and Club-tailed Dragonfly. Occasionally Beautiful D.

Look for them on riverside vegetation, males often on over-hanging branches. They have a more widespread distribution than Beautiful D.

Dragonflies are susceptible to predation by birds, in this instance a Spotted Flycatcher is the culprit.

Males are territorial, gathering on emergent plants and defending the immediate area vigorously.

Family LESTIDAE

Emerald Damselfly

Lestes sponsa

Similar species – Scarce Emerald Damselfly.
Jizz – Elongated, thin needle-like, twinkling flight.
Size – L-38mm, W 38-46mm
Flight period – Late June – end Sept
Status – Very widespread.
First impression – Large. The metallic green colouring combined with clear half opened wings makes it very distinctive.

One of two metallic green damselflies with clear wings. Scarce Emerald Damselfly looks very similar. Take your time with identification if you think that both species are present, it can be tricky, but far from impossible in the field. Males can initially be confused with Blue-tailed Damselfly (look at the colour of the abdomen) and females with female Banded Demoiselle (look at the wing colour).

Eyes bright blue.

At first sides of thorax are yellow, becoming blue with age, along with segments 1,2,8,9 and 10.

Segment 2.
All blue.

Abdomen metallic green/bronze.

MATURE MALE
– In typical wings half open pose.

C.p. markings on 2nd segments of female Emerald, triangular and Scarce Emerald, square.

MATURE FEMALE

Behaviour – Look for males and females secreted among emergent vegetation, they give themselves away as they flit between plants. Mating usually takes place among plants around the water's edge, though some may drift away from the breeding site. The pair work their way down a plant stem in tandem, until both are submerged, laying eggs into the plant above and below the water-line. They can stay under water for up to 30 minutes, using air trapped in their body hairs.

Habitat – Ditches, bog pools, canals, ponds, lakes and other static water, sometimes chocked with weed. Occasionally by slow flowing streams. Shallow water with tall vegetation preferred.

Often found with – Most species. In the north Four-spotted Chaser and Black Darter.

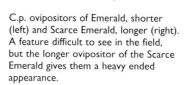

C.p. ovipositors of Emerald, shorter (left) and Scarce Emerald, longer (right). A feature difficult to see in the field, but the longer ovipositor of the Scarce Emerald gives them a heavy ended appearance.

Occasionally females will egg-lay on their own. In this case an older brown individual. The eggs are diapause, so those that are laid above the water will only hatch if enough water fills the pool to cover them before the following spring.

Family LESTIDAE

Scarce Emerald Damselfly

Lestes dryas

Similar species – Emerald Damselfly.
Jizz – Metallic tube, robust, strong.
Size – L-38, W-40-50mm
Flight period – End June – end Aug
Status – Rare (41).
First impression – Large. Again the metallic green colour and clear half opened wings, point towards it being a *Lestes* type. The bright colour and solid appearance make an immediate impact.

Emerald, longer and thinner.

C.p. pterostigmas, Scarce Emerald, shorter and squarer.

MATURE MALE

This rare damselfly is confined to small areas of East Anglia and Essex. It was thought to be extinct in the 1970's, but it's retiring nature probably led to it being overlooked, rather than it recolonising. It can occur with Emerald Damselfly, so the opportunity for close study should not be missed.

Where found, Scarce Emerald can appear in dense numbers, suggesting it is not very territorial.

C.p. shape of male inferior anal appendages. Emerald, straight (left). Scarce Emerald, clubbed (right).

The blue pruinescence covers only about half of the 2nd segment, compared to all on Emerald D.

Some mature males show a fantastic metallic orange/bronze coloration in place of the metallic green.

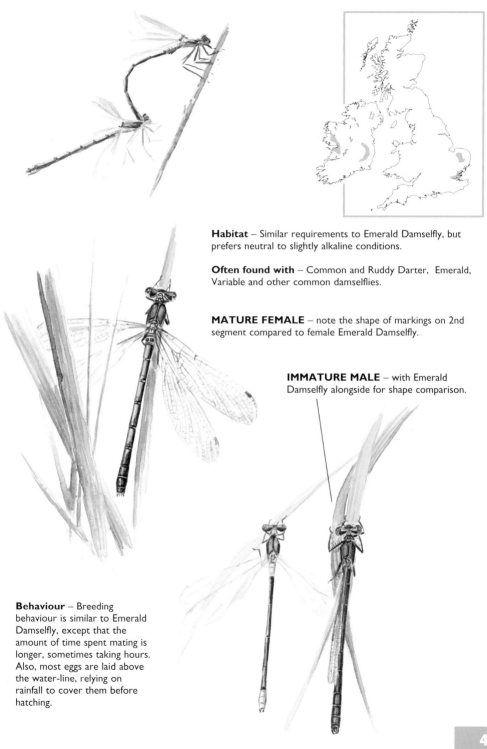

Habitat – Similar requirements to Emerald Damselfly, but prefers neutral to slightly alkaline conditions.

Often found with – Common and Ruddy Darter, Emerald, Variable and other common damselflies.

MATURE FEMALE – note the shape of markings on 2nd segment compared to female Emerald Damselfly.

IMMATURE MALE – with Emerald Damselfly alongside for shape comparison.

Behaviour – Breeding behaviour is similar to Emerald Damselfly, except that the amount of time spent mating is longer, sometimes taking hours. Also, most eggs are laid above the water-line, relying on rainfall to cover them before hatching.

Family COENAGRIONIDAE
Large Red Damselfly
Pyrrhosoma nymphula

Similar species – Small Red Damselfly.
Jizz – Robust, richly coloured, gregarious.
Size – L-36mm, W-38-48mm
Flight period – Late Apr – late Sept
Status – Very widespread.
First impression – Medium sized. Their deep red colour with bronze/black and yellow markings, should make for simple identification.

Red antehumeral stripes.

Black legs

An early synchronised emergence means that this damselfly will probably be the first species that you will encounter, at the start of a new season.

Look for them (often in large numbers) on fringing plants, though immatures may venture further afield.

MATURE MALE

MATURE MALE

One of only two red damselflies found in Great Britain, Large Red Damselfly should not pose too many identification headaches. Large Red D. is Common and widespread, Small Red D. is scarce and more habitat restricted. Large Red D. is robust, with black legs, broad red antehumeral stripes and males have dark markings on the end of the abdomen. Small Red D. is slender, with red legs, no antehumeral stripes and males have a brighter all red abdomen.
Males are territorial and will defend a site from a prominent perch.

Segments 7-9 with bronze/black markings on top.

Behaviour – Egg-laying damselflies can be given away by the light catching their shimmering wings. The male Large Red D. remains clasped to the female as she oviposits into floating leaves and plant stems. The larvae develop over the next 2-3 years.

Habitat – Wide ranging, including acid bogs, streams and rivers. Can tolerate slightly polluted water bodies.

Often found with – Virtually all other Dragonflies.

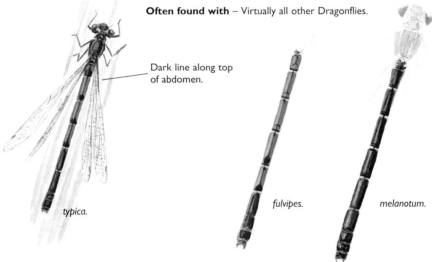

Dark line along top of abdomen.

typica.

fulvipes.

melanotum.

MATURE FEMALES – are more robust in shape than males. Apart from *typica*, females are represented by two other less common colour forms, *fulvipes* and *melanotum*. *Melanotum* may be confused with Red-eyed D. which has blue between the end segments as opposed to red.

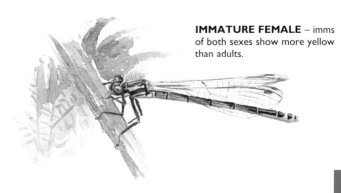

IMMATURE FEMALE – imms of both sexes show more yellow than adults.

Family COENAGRIONIDAE

Small Red Damselfly

Ceriagrion tenellum

Similar species – Large Red Damselfly.
Jizz – Dainty, graceful, glowing.
Size – L-31, W-30-40mm
Flight period – Early Jun – early Sept
Status – Scarce (3,49,68,85,103).
First impression – Small and bright. The red legs give them a more delicate feel compared with the black legs of the robust Large Red D.

C.p. size of Large Red D.(left), which is thicker and tends to be longer.

Due to habitat and climate requirements Small Red D. has a more restricted distribution and is a scarce species compared with Large Red D. Look for them tucked away on fringing vegetation. It may take a little while to tune into them, particularly if the charismatic Golden-ringed Dragonfly and fidgety Keeled Skimmers are busy dashing about catching your attention.

MATURE MALES – N.b. red legs, not black, no antehumeral stripes, all red abdomen with no dark markings on the end, more brightly coloured red, not a deep red.

Behaviour – Males are territorial and like other damselflies will wing flick at intruders. If this fails to deter, then they will fly up and physically force them away.

A sedate mating takes place, lasting from 40-90 mins. Eggs are laid in tandem into submerged plants. Larvae develop over 2 years.

A hunting technique employed by damselflies is to fly at and bump into plants, in an effort to flush prey out.

Habitat – Lowland heaths with shallow bog pools and small streams with sphagnum moss. Also peaty ditches on cut-over bogs and fens.

Often found with – Large Red, Southern and Scarce Blue-tailed Damselfly, Golden-ringed Dragonfly and Keeled Skimmer on runnels. On static heathland ponds Emerald Damselfly, Common Hawker and Black Darter.

MATURE FEMALES

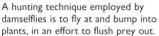

erythrogastrum.   *melanogastrum.*

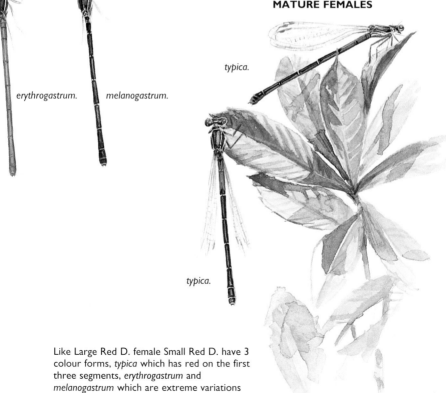

typica.

typica.

Like Large Red D. female Small Red D. have 3 colour forms, *typica* which has red on the first three segments, *erythrogastrum* and *melanogastrum* which are extreme variations of *typica*.

White-legged Damselfly

Platycnemis pennipes

Similar species – Pale immature Common Blue
Damselfly.
Jizz – Delicate, ghostly, elegant.
Size – L-36mm, W-38-46mm
Flight period – Late May – mid Aug
Status – Scarce (7,29,37,38,74,89).
First impression – Medium sized. A striking pale
damselfly.

At first White-legged D. looks like other "blue" damselflies,
but the pastel colouring of the abdomen with markings
running along rather than across it, added to the pale
"swollen" legs of the males, should distinguish White-legged
D. from the others.

A local species with a central southerly distribution. Look
for colonies in vegetation along sunlit lowland streams and
rivers. If flushed they have an annoying tendency to fly off
high.

Abdomen – colour varies from a pale
cream to pastel blue. The amount of
black markings varies with age.

**MATURE
MALES**

Behaviour – Once a female has been
successfully selected and displayed to,
mating takes place for up to 30 mins in
surrounding vegetation. Eggs are laid in
tandem into floating plants and like
other damselflies can be seen doing
this in numbers. The larvae then take
2 years to develop.

Detail of leg, showing
swollen tibia.

Apart from the demoiselles, White-legged D. is unique in having a courtship display. With a bouncy flight a male finds a female and if the responses are right then a fluttering, legs dangling display is performed in front of her.

The display is also employed in territorial disputes between males and may account for the number of males with missing legs.

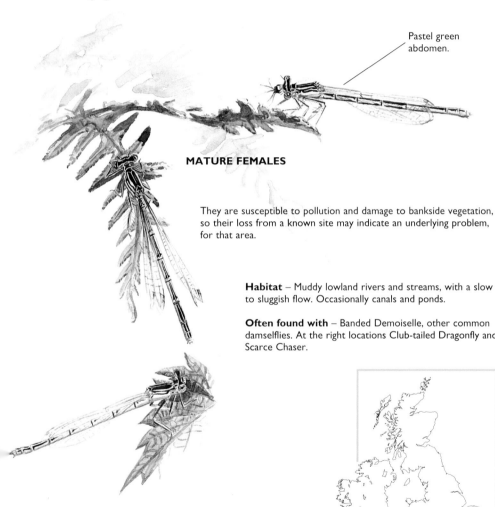

Pastel green abdomen.

MATURE FEMALES

They are susceptible to pollution and damage to bankside vegetation, so their loss from a known site may indicate an underlying problem, for that area.

Habitat – Muddy lowland rivers and streams, with a slow to sluggish flow. Occasionally canals and ponds.

Often found with – Banded Demoiselle, other common damselflies. At the right locations Club-tailed Dragonfly and Scarce Chaser.

IMMATURE – *lactea* form.
N.b. very pale with few markings.

Family COENAGRIONIDAE
Common Blue Damselfly
Enallagma cyathigerum

Similar species – Other blue damselflies.
Jizz – Robust, bright and bold.
Size – L-32mm, W-36-42mm
Flight period – Mid May – mid Sept
Status – Very widespread.
First impression – Medium sized. Strong flyer. The broad antehumeral stripes stand out on both sexes. Not as bright as Azure D.

The ghostly colour of **Immature males** may cause confusion with White-legged D. look at the different abdominal markings to separate them

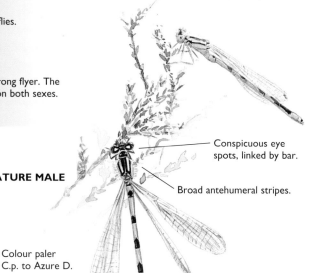

MATURE MALE

Conspicuous eye spots, linked by bar.

Broad antehumeral stripes.

Colour paler
C.p. to Azure D.

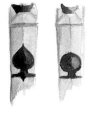

Male – 2nd segments, showing variation in "spot" marking.

Segments 8 & 9 all blue.

N.b. Short stripe (can be difficult to see) on the side of the thorax, all other blue damselflies, have two stripes and they are longer.

MATURE FEMALE
– typical green form.

Unlike dragonflies, male damselflies transfer sperm after a female has been grasped. Mating usually take place away from water, lasting about 20mins.

FEMALE – Detail showing the spine unique to Common Blue D., absent among other "blue" damselflies.

Behaviour – Females oviposit in tandem into the stems of aquatic plants. If she submerges to oviposit the male will detach himself. The female can remain underwater for up to 40 mins. On resurfacing females find it difficult to break free of the water and are prone to predation by fish or birds, unless the original male or an opportunistic interloper pulls her out. Larvae develop over one year or longer if further north.

Habitats – Wide ranging.

Often found with – Most other Dragonflies. Occurs in the same habitat as Northern Damselfly, so take care with identification at Scottish locations.

Look for this very widespread damselfly among sparse waterside vegetation and swarming in their 100's out over the water. Maturing individuals can be found well away from water.

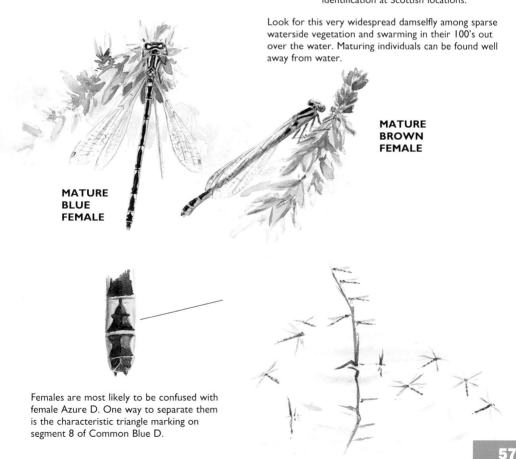

MATURE BLUE FEMALE

MATURE BROWN FEMALE

Females are most likely to be confused with female Azure D. One way to separate them is the characteristic triangle marking on segment 8 of Common Blue D.

Family COENAGRIONIDAE
Azure Damselfly
Coenagrion puella

Similar species – Other blue damselflies.
Particularly Variable Damselfly.
Jizz – Bright, gregarious, swarms.
Size – L-33mm, W-36-44mm
Flight period – Mid May – late Aug
Status – Very widespread.
First impression – Medium sized. The thinner
antehumeral stripes separate it from Common Blue
Damselfly. The greater amount of blue on segment 6
helps when sorting them from Variable Damselfly.

**MATURE
BLUE
FEMALE**
– very
similar to
female
Variable D.

Bright eye spots, not
joined by a bar.
Narrow antehumeral
stripes, sometimes
incomplete.

Look for this damselfly perched among
the shelter vegetation of a water body,
often on the side facing the sun. Large
numbers can be found ovipositing in
quieter areas of open waters. Not as
widespread as Common Blue D.

N.b. two black lines on side of
thorax – only one short black
line on Common Blue D.

**MATURE
GREEN
FEMALE**

No spine under segment 8.

Behaviour – After a lengthy mating, egg-
laying takes place in tandem into aquatic
plants, females sometime submerge alone.
Larvae develop over one year.

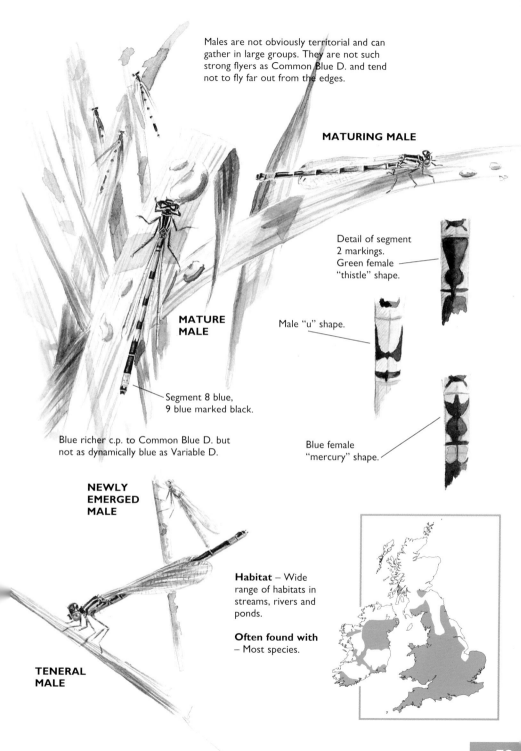

Males are not obviously territorial and can gather in large groups. They are not such strong flyers as Common Blue D. and tend not to fly far out from the edges.

MATURING MALE

MATURE MALE

Detail of segment 2 markings. Green female "thistle" shape.

Male "u" shape.

Segment 8 blue, 9 blue marked black.

Blue female "mercury" shape.

Blue richer c.p. to Common Blue D. but not as dynamically blue as Variable D.

NEWLY EMERGED MALE

Habitat – Wide range of habitats in streams, rivers and ponds.

Often found with – Most species.

TENERAL MALE

Family COENAGRIONIDAE
Variable Damselfly
Coenagrion pulchellum

Similar species – Other blue species. Especially Azure Damselfly.
Jizz – Dark, striking, dynamic.
Size – L-33mm, W-32-42mm
Flight period – Late May – early Aug
Status – Local (7,111,118).
First impression – Medium sized. Aptly named because of the varied amounts of blue and black. Intensely coloured. The smaller amount of blue on segment 6 gives them a "blue-tailed" impression.

A localised species, that is usually found in dense clusters where there is sheltered vegetation at a suitable water body. The only other blue damselflies likely to be encountered with them are Common Blue and Azure Damselfly. Immatures can be found away from water.

Detail of variable thickened "wine glass" markings on 2nd segment, the "stem" may be absent, though the remaining mark is still broad.

Generally no line between eye spots.

6.

Segment 8 blue.
9 black blue.

C.p. end of abdomen markings, Azure (left) and Variable (right) which has more black on segment 6 giving a "blue-tailed" effect.

MATURE MALE

Thorax – "exclamation marks", length varies.

Abdomen – kingfisher blue.

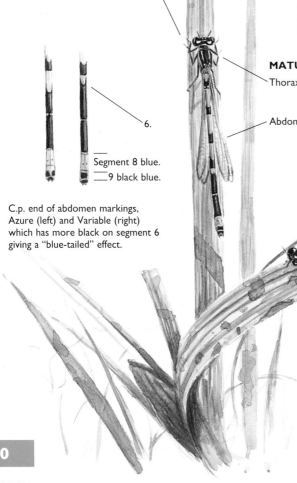

MATURE MALE
– wing flicking aggressively at a rival male.

Behaviour – After a short time mating, females lay their eggs in tandem into the underside of leaves of floating plants, often gathering into large egg-laying groups on the water. Larvae develop over one year.

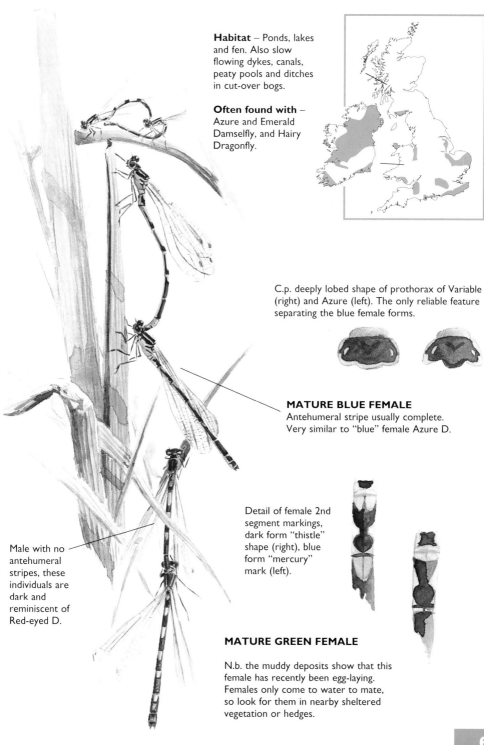

Habitat – Ponds, lakes and fen. Also slow flowing dykes, canals, peaty pools and ditches in cut-over bogs.

Often found with – Azure and Emerald Damselfly, and Hairy Dragonfly.

C.p. deeply lobed shape of prothorax of Variable (right) and Azure (left). The only reliable feature separating the blue female forms.

MATURE BLUE FEMALE
Antehumeral stripe usually complete. Very similar to "blue" female Azure D.

Detail of female 2nd segment markings, dark form "thistle" shape (right), blue form "mercury" mark (left).

Male with no antehumeral stripes, these individuals are dark and reminiscent of Red-eyed D.

MATURE GREEN FEMALE

N.b. the muddy deposits show that this female has recently been egg-laying. Females only come to water to mate, so look for them in nearby sheltered vegetation or hedges.

Family COENAGRIONIDAE
Southern Damselfly
Coenagrion mercuriale

Similar species – Other blue damselflies.
Jizz – Secretive, retiring, needle-like.
Size – L-29mm, W-30-36mm
Flight period – Mid May – early Aug
Status – Rare (8,25,49,51,68,96).
First impression – Once your eyes tune in, their small stature is very helpful with identification.

Detail of thorax of mature female.

MATURE MALE
with Azure D. alongside for size c.p.

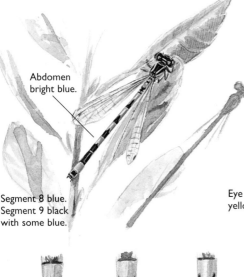

Abdomen bright blue.

Segment 8 blue.
Segment 9 black with some blue.

Males fly slowly, perching on low sunlit vegetation along the edges of streams. Unless looking to mate females are usually seen away from the breeding areas, on nearby heathland or meadows. Southern D. is not likely to be encountered with any other blue damselflies, though the ranges of Common Blue and Azure overlap with it.

Southern D. has a scattered southerly distribution and is protected under the wildlife and countryside act.

Eye spots vary in colour from yellow/green to blue.

Detail of 2nd male segments showing variable "mercury" mark.

MATURE GREEN FEMALE
N.b. small amount of bl[ue] between end segments.

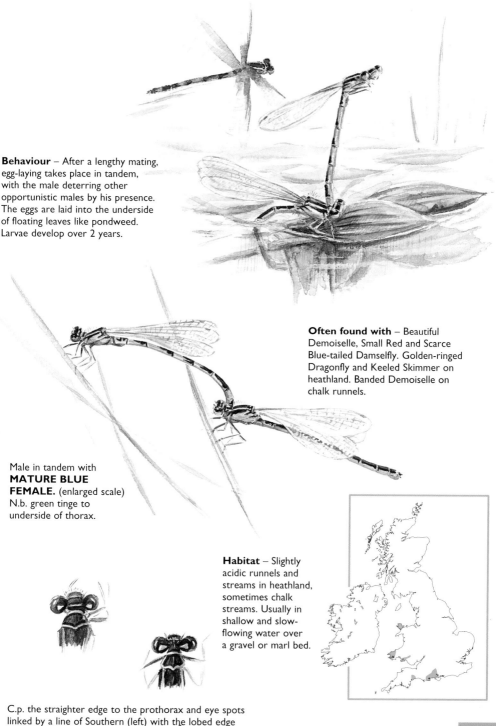

Behaviour – After a lengthy mating, egg-laying takes place in tandem, with the male deterring other opportunistic males by his presence. The eggs are laid into the underside of floating leaves like pondweed. Larvae develop over 2 years.

Often found with – Beautiful Demoiselle, Small Red and Scarce Blue-tailed Damselfly. Golden-ringed Dragonfly and Keeled Skimmer on heathland. Banded Demoiselle on chalk runnels.

Male in tandem with **MATURE BLUE FEMALE.** (enlarged scale) N.b. green tinge to underside of thorax.

Habitat – Slightly acidic runnels and streams in heathland, sometimes chalk streams. Usually in shallow and slow-flowing water over a gravel or marl bed.

C.p. the straighter edge to the prothorax and eye spots linked by a line of Southern (left) with the lobed edge and no line between eye spots of Azure (right).

Family COENAGRIONIDAE
Northern Damselfly
Coenagrion hastulatum

Similar species – Other blue damselflies.
Jizz – Secretive, inconspicuous and weak flyer.
Size – L-31mm, W-34-44mm
Flight period – Late May – early Aug
Status – Very rare (63).
First impression – Smallish sized. Similar in behaviour to Southern Damselfly. The green tinge to the blue on the thorax stands out.

Look out for this shy species as it flies weakly, low down among the vegetation at or near the water's edge. Northern D. has a very local Scottish distribution and is not numerous at these sites. Common Blue D. is the only other blue damselfly likely to be seen with Northern D., but with care should not cause too many identification problems. Common Blue D. is stronger in flight, dashing out over open water. Immatures can be seen further away from the pool often resting in sheltered glades.

Two black lines on side of thorax, only one short black line on Common Blue D.

Thorax tinged green. Stands out in flight.

MATURE MALE

Black dash on side of segment 2.

Eye spots joined by line.

MATURE MALE

Segment 8 blue.
Segment 9 blue, slightly marked black, though can be absent.

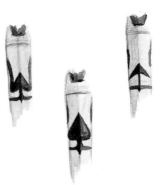

Detail of male 2nd segments, showing variable "arrowhead" marking.

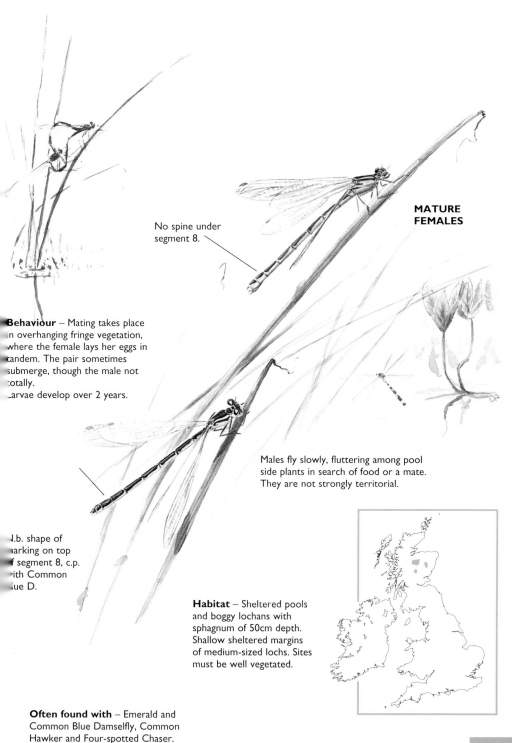

No spine under segment 8.

MATURE FEMALES

Behaviour – Mating takes place in overhanging fringe vegetation, where the female lays her eggs in tandem. The pair sometimes submerge, though the male not totally.
Larvae develop over 2 years.

Males fly slowly, fluttering among pool side plants in search of food or a mate. They are not strongly territorial.

N.b. shape of marking on top of segment 8, c.p. with Common Blue D.

Habitat – Sheltered pools and boggy lochans with sphagnum of 50cm depth. Shallow sheltered margins of medium-sized lochs. Sites must be well vegetated.

Often found with – Emerald and Common Blue Damselfly, Common Hawker and Four-spotted Chaser.

Family COENAGRIONIDAE
Irish Damselfly
Coenagrion lunulatum

Similar species – Other blue damselflies.
Jizz – Distinctive, dark, banded.
Size – L-33mm, W-32-38mm
Flight period – Mid May – early July
Status – Rare.
First impression – Smallish. Mainly black on the abdomen with thin blue hoops and "blue-tailed" appearance.

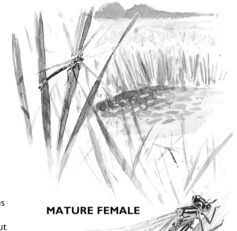

Only discovered in Ireland in 1981, this distinctive species may yet be found on this side of the Irish Sea, where suitable similar habitats occur in the north-west. Look out for males sat out on floating plants in the pools.

Irish D. is most like Northern D., but the overall darker appearance, greener underside and different segment 2 markings of Irish D. should help to separate them.

MATURE FEMALE

C.p. pointed shape on segment 8 with Northern D.

MATURE MALES

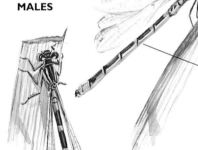

Underside characteristically green.

N.b. square shaped lobe on prothorax.

Top of the abdomen distinctive. Mostly black with blue hoops.

Segment 8 blue.
Segment 9 blue.

Often found with – Variable Damselfly. Hairy Dragonfly and Common Hawker.

Habitat – Slightly alkaline lakes, such as open pools in valley fens. Also in small peaty, mildly acidic pools.

MALE detail of segment 2 "crescent" shape.

COMPARISON GUIDE TO MALE BLUE DAMSELFLIES.

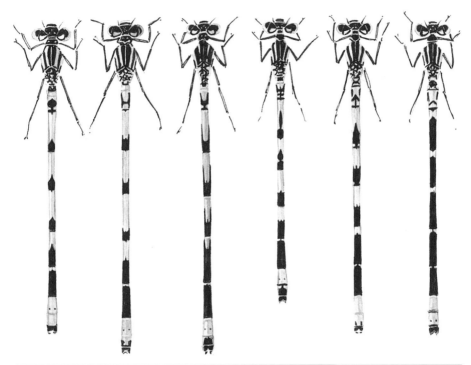

Common Blue D. "spot"	Azure D. "u"	Variable D. "wine glass"	Southern D. "mercury"	Northern D. "arrowhead"	Irish D. "crescent"	
nearly all blue, small amount of black.	nearly all blue, black "u" shaped.	mostly blue, black "u" shaped.	blue, with black "spear" shape.	blue, with black "spearhead".	nearly all black, small blue hoop.	]3
blue.	blue.	blue.	blue.	blue.	blue.	]8
blue.	blue, marked black.	mainly black, some blue.	mainly black, marked blue.	blue, small amount of black.	blue.	]9

The row of species names has bracket]2 to the right.

Blue-tailed Damselfly

Ischnura elegans

Similar species – Scarce Blue-tailed & Red-eyed Damselfly.
Jizz – Little blue beacons, gregarious steady flyer.
Size – L-31mm, W-30-40mm
Flight period – Early May – early Sept
Status – Very widespread.
First impression – Medium sized. Dark with bright blue "tail lights", can appear in a variety of colour forms. Probably the first damselfly you will come across.

MATURE MALE

Blue "tail light" band on segment 8 only.

Likely to be the first coloniser of a newly constructed pond in your back garden, often perching on windows and the side of buildings.

MATURE MALE
in threat posture.

A widespread species that give themselves away by their bright blue "tail light" shinning out from waterside plants. Females show a range of stunning colour forms, probably related to age. Apart from "colonising" individuals, all sexes and ages tend to be found together.

IMMATURE MALE
with green thorax.

Blue-tails are only likely to be confused with the much rarer Scarce Blue-tailed D. and Red-eyed D. It is bulkier in appearance c.p. to Scarce Blue-tailed D. and has different "tail" markings. It is not as powerful looking as Red Eyed D. which has red eyes, and a greyer, not black, blue tipped abdomen.

Female colour forms.
rufescens.

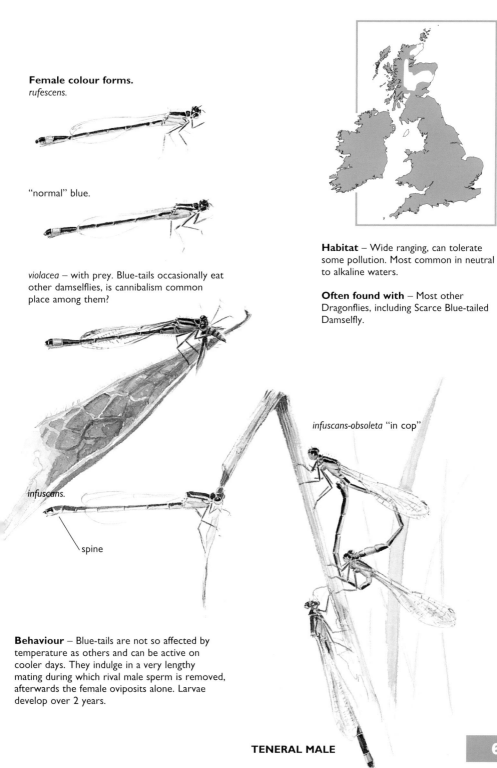

"normal" blue.

violacea – with prey. Blue-tails occasionally eat other damselflies, is cannibalism common place among them?

infuscans.

spine

Habitat – Wide ranging, can tolerate some pollution. Most common in neutral to alkaline waters.

Often found with – Most other Dragonflies, including Scarce Blue-tailed Damselfly.

infuscans-obsoleta "in cop"

Behaviour – Blue-tails are not so affected by temperature as others and can be active on cooler days. They indulge in a very lengthy mating during which rival male sperm is removed, afterwards the female oviposits alone. Larvae develop over 2 years.

TENERAL MALE

69

Family COENAGRIONIDAE

Scarce Blue-tailed Damselfly

Ischnura pumilio

Similar species – Blue-tailed & Red-eyed Damselfly.
Jizz – Weak, diminutive, skulking, jerky flyer.
Size – L-29mm, W-28-36mm
Flight period – Late May – early Sept
Status – Scarce (68).
First impression – Small. Similar to Blue-tailed overall, but skulks low down in emergent foliage.

MATURE MALE

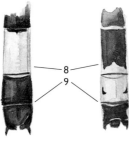

C.p. distribution of blue on the end segments. Blue-tailed D (left). Scarce Blue-tailed D (middle and right). Amount of black can vary on 9.

C.p. size between Blue-tailed D. (top) and Scarce Blue-tailed D. (below). N.b. the size can vary greatly between individual Blue-tailed D. but they are always bulkier.

C.p. shape of pterostigmas, Scarce Blue-tailed D. (above), Blue-tailed D. (below).

The first problem to overcome with this species is to find one! they really are small and like to hide behind stems. Look for movement as they fly low down among short growing plants, at the edge of and in the pool. If disturbed too much they seek shelter in larger nearby bushes. However pioneering individuals are capable of a strong vertical flight and are thus carried off on the wind. This aids with the dispersal of the species in case the home pool dries out. It is a rare species with a localised south-west distribution, though other populations may be being overlooked, because of their retiring nature.

Habitat – Slow flowing mineral-enriched seepages, runnels and streams, also shallow flashes and ponds. Amazingly sometimes at spring lines at industrial workings, such as quarries. Can tolerate acid and alkaline waters.

Often found with – Southern, Blue-tailed and Small Red Damselfly. Broad-bodied Chaser and Common Darter.

Behaviour – Copulation lasts about 1-2 hours, after which the female egg-lays alone, although the male may take on a roving protector role. Larvae develop over one year.

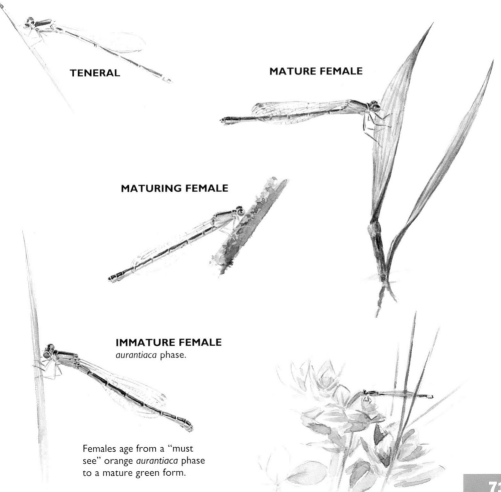

TENERAL

MATURE FEMALE

MATURING FEMALE

IMMATURE FEMALE
aurantiaca phase.

Females age from a "must see" orange *aurantiaca* phase to a mature green form.

Family COENAGRIONIDAE

Red-eyed Damselfly

Erythromma najas

Similar species – Scarce Blue-tailed & Blue-tailed Damselfly.
Jizz – Rapid, zippy, powerful.
Size – L-35mm, W-38-48mm
Flight period – Mid May – mid Aug
Status – Local (7,29,49,73,108,115,122).
First impression – Larger sized. A dark species, the bright red eyes stand out. Typically they like to sit out on Lily pads. An exciting damselfly to watch.

The males of this robust damselfly sit out on floating plants, dashing out on territorial or hunting forays. Look for females sat on marginal plants. They have a southern localised distribution.

Male agitated by the presence of another on his Lily pad.

MATURE MALE

Blue tip, not band.

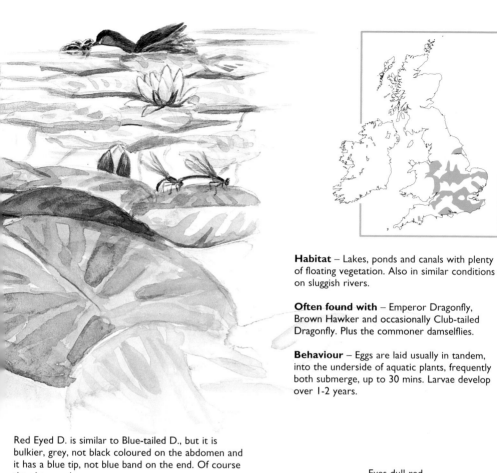

Habitat – Lakes, ponds and canals with plenty of floating vegetation. Also in similar conditions on sluggish rivers.

Often found with – Emperor Dragonfly, Brown Hawker and occasionally Club-tailed Dragonfly. Plus the commoner damselflies.

Behaviour – Eggs are laid usually in tandem, into the underside of aquatic plants, frequently both submerge, up to 30 mins. Larvae develop over 1-2 years.

Red Eyed D. is similar to Blue-tailed D., but it is bulkier, grey, not black coloured on the abdomen and it has a blue tip, not blue band on the end. Of course they have red eyes.

Immatures of male and female start out yellow in colour.

Eyes dull red.

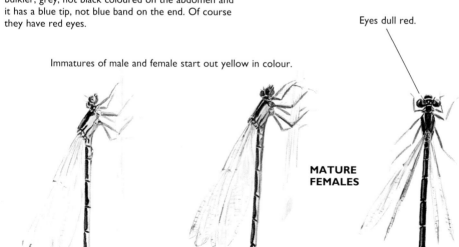

MATURE FEMALES

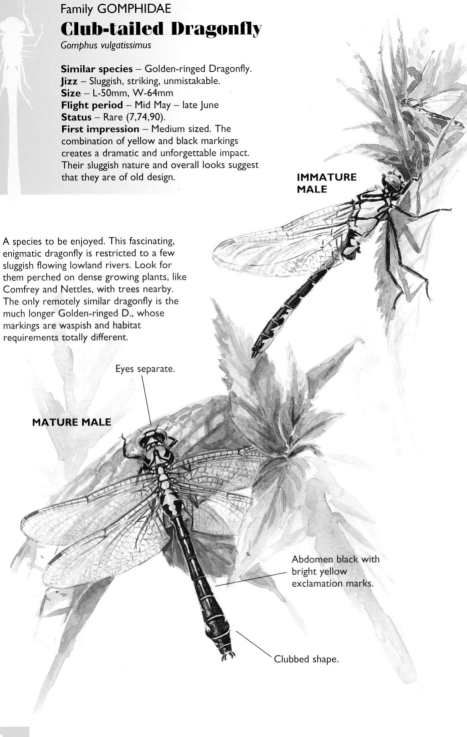

Family GOMPHIDAE

Club-tailed Dragonfly

Gomphus vulgatissimus

Similar species – Golden-ringed Dragonfly.
Jizz – Sluggish, striking, unmistakable.
Size – L-50mm, W-64mm
Flight period – Mid May – late June
Status – Rare (7,74,90).
First impression – Medium sized. The
combination of yellow and black markings
creates a dramatic and unforgettable impact.
Their sluggish nature and overall looks suggest
that they are of old design.

**IMMATURE
MALE**

A species to be enjoyed. This fascinating,
enigmatic dragonfly is restricted to a few
sluggish flowing lowland rivers. Look for
them perched on dense growing plants, like
Comfrey and Nettles, with trees nearby.
The only remotely similar dragonfly is the
much longer Golden-ringed D., whose
markings are waspish and habitat
requirements totally different.

Eyes separate.

MATURE MALE

Abdomen black with
bright yellow
exclamation marks.

Clubbed shape.

Habitat – Moderate to slow flowing rivers with a silt or mud bottom.

Often found with – Banded Demoiselle, White-legged and at some sites Red-eyed Damselfly.

Behaviour – An opportunity to observe a 100 or so larvae creeping out from a river and emerging as superb adult insects, is one to be savoured and never forgotten. The immatures harden off on bankside vegetation and when ready, fly off slowly into the trees. Some journey up to 10 kms away, where they mature in woodland glades and rides. A week or so later they return to the river to breed. Mating takes place in bankside vegetation, after which the female lays her eggs alone, by dipping her abdomen into the river. The eggs are washed off and float down into the muddy bottom. Larvae develop over 4 years.

C.p. angular shape of hindwing male (right) with the rounded shape of female (left).

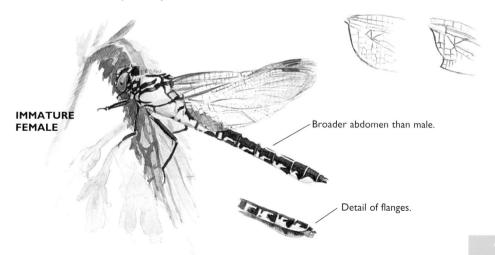

IMMATURE FEMALE

Broader abdomen than male.

Detail of flanges.

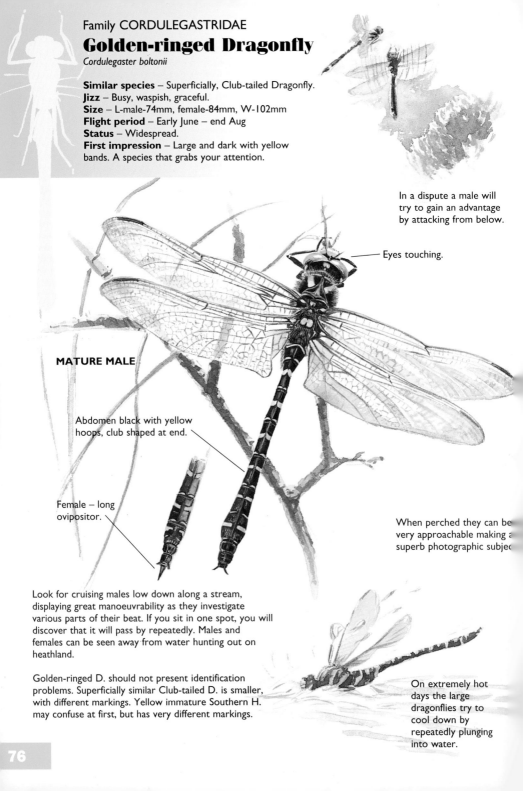

Family CORDULEGASTRIDAE
Golden-ringed Dragonfly
Cordulegaster boltonii

Similar species – Superficially, Club-tailed Dragonfly.
Jizz – Busy, waspish, graceful.
Size – L-male-74mm, female-84mm, W-102mm
Flight period – Early June – end Aug
Status – Widespread.
First impression – Large and dark with yellow
bands. A species that grabs your attention.

In a dispute a male will
try to gain an advantage
by attacking from below.

Eyes touching.

MATURE MALE

Abdomen black with yellow
hoops, club shaped at end.

Female – long
ovipositor.

When perched they can be
very approachable making a
superb photographic subject

Look for cruising males low down along a stream,
displaying great manoeuvrability as they investigate
various parts of their beat. If you sit in one spot, you will
discover that it will pass by repeatedly. Males and
females can be seen away from water hunting out on
heathland.

Golden-ringed D. should not present identification
problems. Superficially similar Club-tailed D. is smaller,
with different markings. Yellow immature Southern H.
may confuse at first, but has very different markings.

On extremely hot
days the large
dragonflies try to
cool down by
repeatedly plunging
into water.

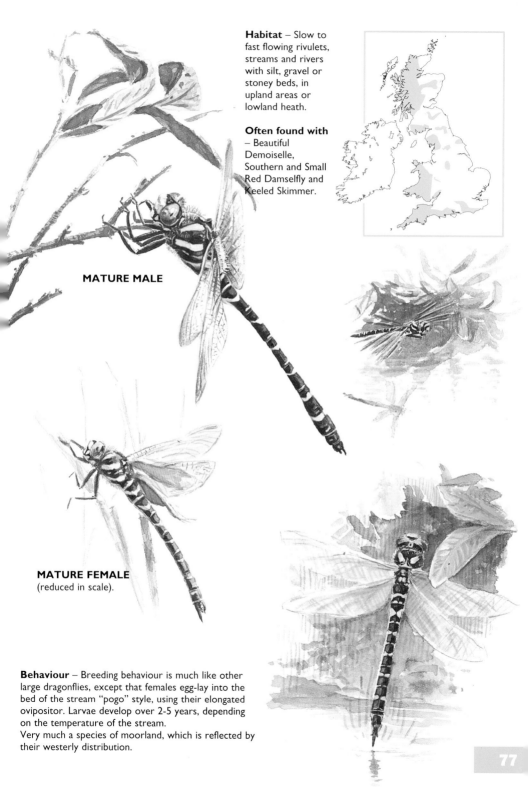

Habitat – Slow to fast flowing rivulets, streams and rivers with silt, gravel or stoney beds, in upland areas or lowland heath.

Often found with – Beautiful Demoiselle, Southern and Small Red Damselfly and Keeled Skimmer.

MATURE MALE

MATURE FEMALE
(reduced in scale).

Behaviour – Breeding behaviour is much like other large dragonflies, except that females egg-lay into the bed of the stream "pogo" style, using their elongated ovipositor. Larvae develop over 2-5 years, depending on the temperature of the stream.
Very much a species of moorland, which is reflected by their westerly distribution.

Family AESHNIDAE
Hairy Dragonfly
Brachytron pratense

Similar species – When first flying nothing, later on other hawker species.
Jizz – Neat, compact, secretive.
Size – L-55mm, W-72mm
Flight period – Early May – late June
Status – Local (8,29,69,96,111,122).
First impression – Small pretty hawker, with neat markings.

A species of early spring, Hairy D. is the first of the hawkers to emerge. Small in stature they should not be too tricky to identify. Their early flight season means that they do not overlap with the similar looking Migrant Hawker. Other hawkers may overlap later on, but they are larger with bolder markings. They may also be seen with Emperor which is much larger and Norfolk H. which is brown.

Downy thorax.

MATURE MALES

Long pterostigmas (dark cells near to the end of the wing).

Long claspers.

Look for males as they patrol low down along ditches weaving in and out of reeds. Check in nearby vegetation for perched males and mating pairs. On one occasion five pairs were disturbed out of a small patch of grass by an apologetic observer! As the day warms, numbers build up and the area will become alive with activity. You may come across immatures and females several kms away in woodland.

Yellow spot on segment one.

Paired blue spots.

Male and female in flight. N.b. females "fat cigar" shape.

Habitat – Ponds, lakes, gravel pits, canals, ditches, marshy fens, and sometimes slow moving rivers.

Often found with – The commoner damsels, Variable and Emerald Damselfly, Four-spotted Chaser. In East Anglia, sometimes Norfolk Hawker.

Mainly a southerly localised distribution.

FEMALE
– with prey.

Behaviour – Mating takes place in nearby vegetation. Females oviposit alone, into floating plants. Larvae develop over 2 years.

Smallish untidy pairs of yellow spots.

Family AESHNIDAE

Azure Hawker

Aeshna caerulea

Similar species – Common Hawker.
Jizz – Electric, dashing, inquisitive.
Size – L-62mm, W-84mm
Flight period – June – late July
Status – Rare (21,95).
First impression – Medium sized
hawker. Males are absolute stunners,
a vivid blue flash.

MATURE MALE – perched on the side of a tree.

Antehumeral stripes
not always obvious.

Regarded by many as the
"Holy Grail" of Dragonflies.
Discovering your own Azure
H. is a joy, the equivalent of a
birder finding a Golden Oriole.

Azure H. is a creature of hot sunny days and can be seen
dashing around pools, an electric blue flash. Difficult to
get close to at rest, but when flying they are inquisitive
and you are likely to be closely scrutinized by one. On
cooler days they like to bask on rocks and are much
more approachable, you may even become a perch
yourself. On dull, cold rainy days, stay in bed.

Abdomen black with
electric blue spots,
when warmed up.

Pale frons.

MATURE MALE – basking
on a rock, wings normally
held forward.

The only other hawker likely to be seen with
Azure is Common, which is larger, darker
looking and has a bright yellow costa.

Abdomen black with pale
blue spots, when cooler.

Look for them also in sheltered woodland glades and rides, where there are boulders. The picture shows an individual searching "Treecreeper fashion" for a resting place on the side of a tree.

It is confined to two main areas of Scotland, the Highlands and further south in Galloway, where they are best sought.

MATURE FEMALES

Brown form –
Abdomen brown
with beige spots.

Blue form –
Abdomen brown
with blue spots.

Behaviour – Males search for a female out over the bog pools. After a short time mating, the female egg-lays alone in shallow sphagnum pools. The eggs are diapause and larvae develop over 2 years.

Habitat – Open moorland with shallow pools, with some sphagnum moss, feeds along rides and glades.

Often found with – Large Red and Emerald Damselfly, Four-spotted Chaser, Black and Highland Darter, Common Hawker and Golden-ringed Dragonfly.

Family AESHNIDAE

Southern Hawker

Aeshna cyanea

Similar species – Common and
Migrant Hawker, Hairy Dragonfly.
Jizz – Bright, colourful, inquisitive.
Size – L-70mm, W-98mm
Flight period – Mid July – end Sept
Status – Very widespread.
First impression – Large. Boldly
patterned. A stunner.

Mature with
brown tinge to
wings.

MATURE MALES

With a southerly distribution, this hawker could be
confused with Hairy D., Migrant and Common
Hawkers and Emperor D.
Southern H. has characteristic broad antehumeral
"headlights" and undivided spots on segments 9
and 10.

Broad antehumeral
"headlights".

Brown costa.

Males patrol a steady beat at about
waist height. They are very
inquisitive and you are likely to be
closely inspected if you encroach
onto a territory.

Undivided blue spots segments 9 and 10.
C.p. with end segments Common H (right).

Large yellow triangle
on segment 2.

Abdomen dark with large apple
green spots.

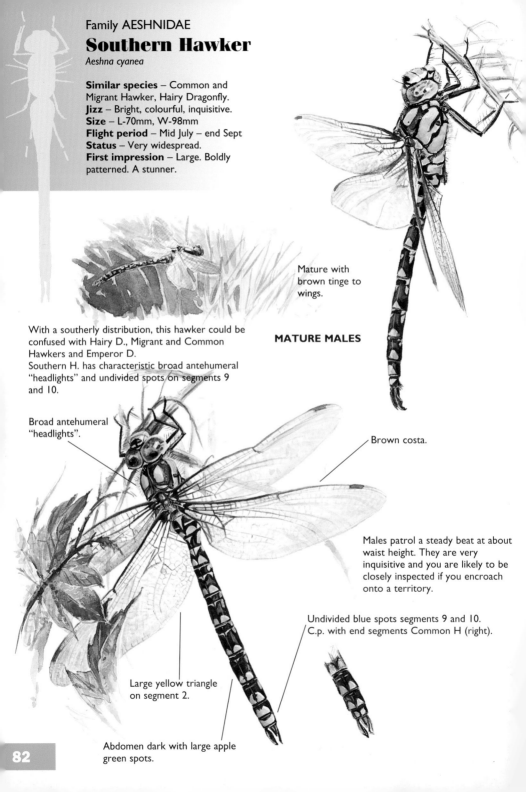

Dragonflies hunt from below, legs held out, with the barbs forming a net. Southern H. are less effected by cool temperatures often flying late in the day.

Behaviour – Males are territorial and avoid too many clashes with rivals, by different males visiting a pond at different times of day. If a female is spotted a frantic chase ensues and if she is clasped, they fly off in the "wheel position" to the tree tops to mate for up to 2 hours. Females egg-lay into a bewildering variety of places, living plants, dead wood, leather shoes and even clothing. Larvae develop over 2 years.

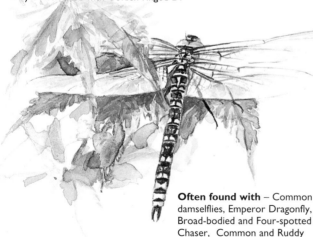

IMMATURE YELLOW FEMALE
May be confused with Golden-ringed D.

MATURE FEMALE
The sound of whirring wings gives away the presence of an egg-laying female.

Often found with – Common damselflies, Emperor Dragonfly, Broad-bodied and Four-spotted Chaser, Common and Ruddy Darter.

They can be found at woodland and urban ponds, or perched in nearby vegetation. Garden ponds are readily used to breed in. Frequently seen away from water in woodland glades, rides and along the sunny side of hedgerows.

Habitat – Mainly neutral to alkaline waters at low altitudes. On ponds, garden pools, canals and ditches.

Family AESHNIDAE

Common Hawker

Aeshna juncea

Similar species – Hairy D., Southern, Migrant and Azure Hawkers.
Jizz – Cautious, wary, strong flyer.
Size – L-74mm, W-95mm
Flight period – Late June – into Oct
Status – Very widespread.
First impression – Large, dark overall appearance. Smaller markings than Southern Hawker, relentless flyer.

Might be confused with Southern and Migrant H. and in Scotland Azure H.
Southern H. has broad antehumeral stripes, a large yellow triangle on segment 2, segments 9 and 10 have blue undivided spots and are green not blue in appearance. Migrant H. is smaller, has a yellow "golf tee" on segment 2 and lacks the bright yellow costa of Common H. Azure H. is smaller with a dull costa and is much brighter coloured.

Males patrol unobtrusively around a pool searching slowly for a mate.

Narrow antehumeral stripes.

Bright yellow costa, sometimes visible in flight.

Narrow yellow mark on segment 2.

MATURE MALES

Abdomen black with smaller pairs of spots, c.p. to Southern H.

Segments 9 and 10 spots divided c.p. to Southern H.

Hunting males fly quite high up c.p. to patrolling males at a pond.

Although it has a very widespread distribution Common H. is not a common dragonfly.

Behaviour – If a female is found at a territory she is quickly grasped by the male and taken away up into trees or nearby vegetation, for up to an hour. Eggs are laid alone into water plants. Larvae develop over 2-5 years, depending on water temperature.

MATURE FEMALE egg-laying.

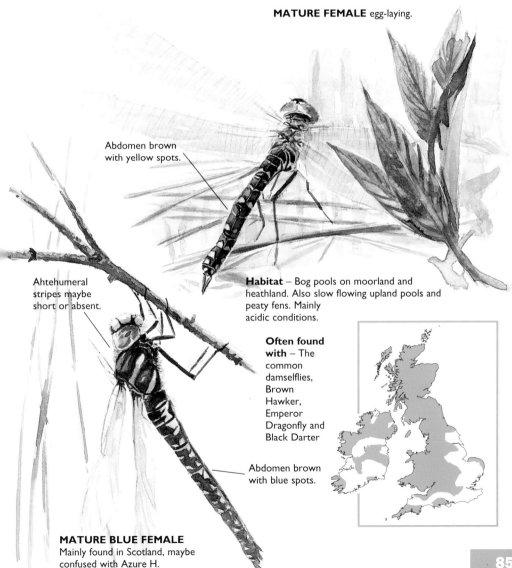

Abdomen brown with yellow spots.

Ahtehumeral stripes maybe short or absent.

Habitat – Bog pools on moorland and heathland. Also slow flowing upland pools and peaty fens. Mainly acidic conditions.

Often found with – The common damselflies, Brown Hawker, Emperor Dragonfly and Black Darter

Abdomen brown with blue spots.

MATURE BLUE FEMALE
Mainly found in Scotland, maybe confused with Azure H.

85

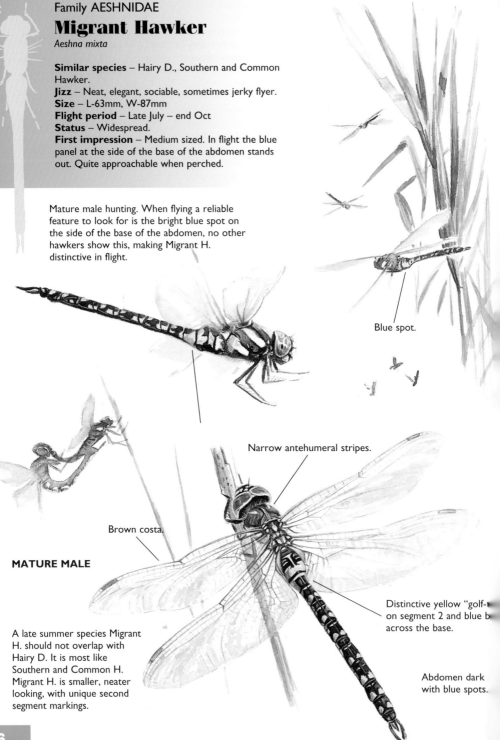

Family AESHNIDAE

Migrant Hawker

Aeshna mixta

Similar species – Hairy D., Southern and Common Hawker.
Jizz – Neat, elegant, sociable, sometimes jerky flyer.
Size – L-63mm, W-87mm
Flight period – Late July – end Oct
Status – Widespread.
First impression – Medium sized. In flight the blue panel at the side of the base of the abdomen stands out. Quite approachable when perched.

Mature male hunting. When flying a reliable feature to look for is the bright blue spot on the side of the base of the abdomen, no other hawkers show this, making Migrant H. distinctive in flight.

Blue spot.

Narrow antehumeral stripes.

Brown costa.

MATURE MALE

A late summer species Migrant H. should not overlap with Hairy D. It is most like Southern and Common H. Migrant H. is smaller, neater looking, with unique second segment markings.

Distinctive yellow "golf-t on segment 2 and blue b across the base.

Abdomen dark with blue spots.

Behaviour – The unique shape and function of the claspers should prevent cross-breeding, however occasionally an enthusiastic male may grab another species. Illustrated is a male Migrant H. with a female Southern H. She rejected him by continually curling up her abdomen, eventually he released her and collapsed into the grass exhausted.

Mating takes place in nearby vegetation for an hour or so. The female usually oviposits alone into floating plants. The eggs are diapause and the larvae develop over the following year.

Migrant Hawker has only recently become a resident species in the south of the country. Earlier records relate to migrants, hence the name. Like Southern H. they are quite likely to turn up in your back garden. Look for them gathering on pools as the day warms, patrolling low down, often hovering to investigate bays and vegetation for females. Counts of 10 males at one pond are not unusual, showing that they are not very territorial. Other parts of the day are spent away from water, often hunting until dusk. They can be found in parks and hedgerows. Check for perched individuals on the sunny side of hedges and banks.

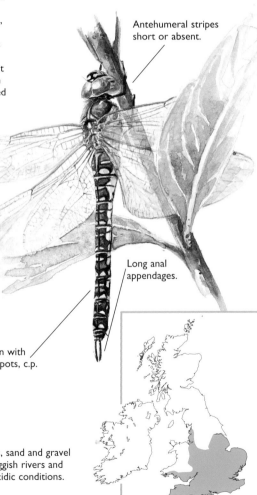

Antehumeral stripes short or absent.

Long anal appendages.

MATURE FEMALE

Abdomen brown with smaller yellow spots, c.p. to male.

Habitat – Ponds, lakes, sand and gravel pits, canals, ditches, sluggish rivers and streams. Avoids very acidic conditions.

Often found with – The common damselflies, Southern, and Brown Hawker, Common and Ruddy Darter.

Family AESHNIDAE
Emperor Dragonfly
Anax imperator

Similar species – The other hawkers.
Jizz – Powerful, dominant.
Size – L-78mm, W-107mm
Flight period – Late May – mid Aug
Status – Widespread.
First impression – Large, impressive.
Males shine Kingfisher blue. They always
make a dramatic impact at a water body.

In pursuit of Large
Red D. n.b. droop
at end of abdomen.

Thorax apple green.

Yellow costa.

MATURE MALE

Abdomen bright enamel-
blue with thick black line
down centre.

Though similar to other
hawkers, Emperor D. can
be separated from the
others by it's large striking
appearance and distinctive
dark stripe down the centre
of the abdomen. Another
species with a southerly
distribution, though on a
steady march northwards.

Males prepare for mating by
transferring sperm in flight
from segment 8 to segment 2.

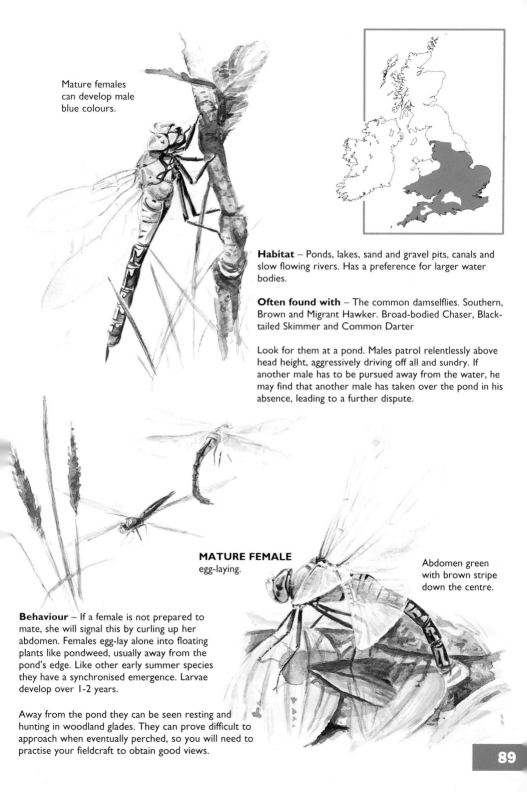

Mature females can develop male blue colours.

Habitat – Ponds, lakes, sand and gravel pits, canals and slow flowing rivers. Has a preference for larger water bodies.

Often found with – The common damselflies. Southern, Brown and Migrant Hawker. Broad-bodied Chaser, Black-tailed Skimmer and Common Darter

Look for them at a pond. Males patrol relentlessly above head height, aggressively driving off all and sundry. If another male has to be pursued away from the water, he may find that another male has taken over the pond in his absence, leading to a further dispute.

MATURE FEMALE
egg-laying.

Abdomen green with brown stripe down the centre.

Behaviour – If a female is not prepared to mate, she will signal this by curling up her abdomen. Females egg-lay alone into floating plants like pondweed, usually away from the pond's edge. Like other early summer species they have a synchronised emergence. Larvae develop over 1-2 years.

Away from the pond they can be seen resting and hunting in woodland glades. They can prove difficult to approach when eventually perched, so you will need to practise your fieldcraft to obtain good views.

Norfolk Hawker

Aeshna isosceles

Similar species – Brown Hawker.
Jizz – Slender, cryptic when perched.
Size – L-67mm, W-93mm
Flight period – Early June – mid July
Status – Very rare (91,101,106).
First impression – Large and slim.
The light brown body, green eyes and
clear wings stand out.

Though superficially similar to Brown,
Norfolk H. differs by being tan brown, having
clear wings and green eyes. With experience,
they should not present any identification
problems.

MALES
in conflict.

Water
Soldier

Norfolk H. is very rare and is confined to a
few sites in East Anglia. It is protected by
the Wildlife and Countryside Act.
Dependent on the presence of Water
Soldier in unpolluted ditches, they are very
vulnerable to changes in their habitat, such
as ditch clearance.
You will find males patrolling along a
chosen length of ditch, frequently clashing
with rival males. They can also be found
further away from water in sheltered
woodland glades.

Detail of characteristic yellow
isosceles marking on segment 2.

The presence of Water Soldier in
a ditch is crucial for successful
egg-laying. Also look for Frog-bit.

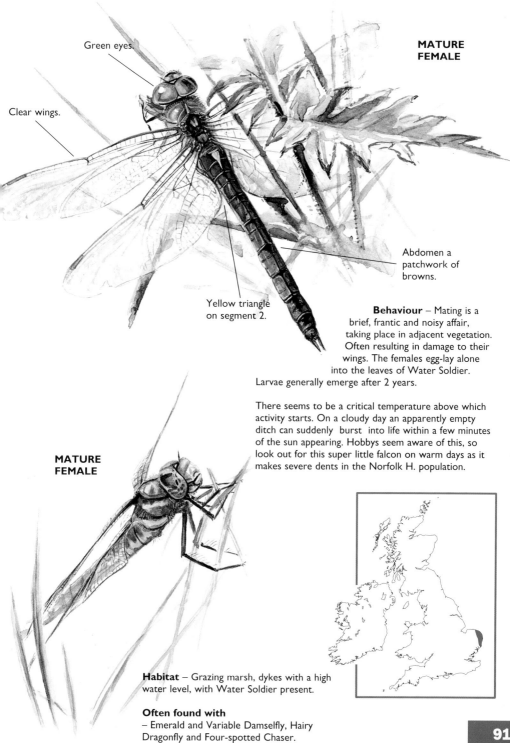

Green eyes.

MATURE FEMALE

Clear wings.

Abdomen a patchwork of browns.

Yellow triangle on segment 2.

Behaviour – Mating is a brief, frantic and noisy affair, taking place in adjacent vegetation. Often resulting in damage to their wings. The females egg-lay alone into the leaves of Water Soldier. Larvae generally emerge after 2 years.

There seems to be a critical temperature above which activity starts. On a cloudy day an apparently empty ditch can suddenly burst into life within a few minutes of the sun appearing. Hobbys seem aware of this, so look out for this super little falcon on warm days as it makes severe dents in the Norfolk H. population.

MATURE FEMALE

Habitat – Grazing marsh, dykes with a high water level, with Water Soldier present.

Often found with – Emerald and Variable Damselfly, Hairy Dragonfly and Four-spotted Chaser.

91

Family AESHNIDAE

Brown Hawker

Aeshna grandis

Similar species – Norfolk Hawker.
Jizz – Glowing, ostentatious, strong.
Size – L-73mm, W-102mm
Flight period – Mid Jun – mid Oct
Status – Very widespread.
First impression – Large. Obvious. The glowing orange wings stand out against the dark body.

An unmistakable species. The only similar species is Norfolk H. which has clear wings, is very rare and is restricted to East Anglia, whereas Brown H. is common in Central and Southern England.

MATURE FEMALE
N.b. yellow markings on thorax.

Blue/brown eyes.

MATURE MALE

Abdomen brown with bright blue spots.

One of Britain's most beautiful Dragonflies, look for them at water bodies, woodland, hedgerows and urban settings. They are tireless flyers. Difficult enough to find, let alone approach when perched, "brown" dragonflies hide very well in green grass!

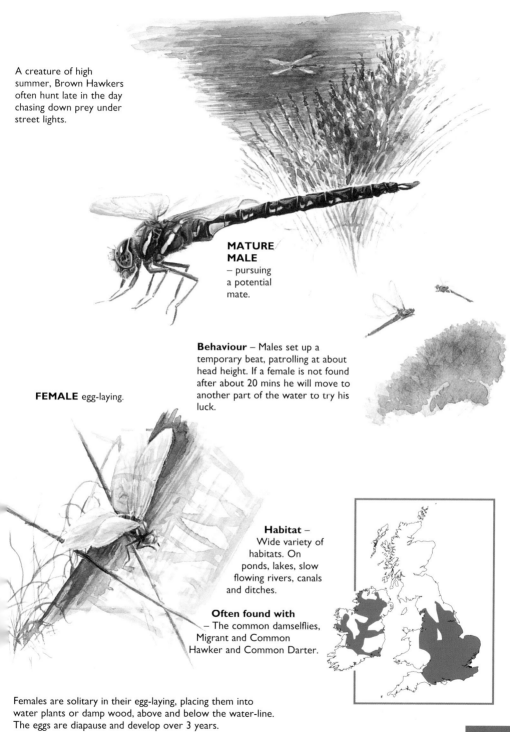

A creature of high summer, Brown Hawkers often hunt late in the day chasing down prey under street lights.

MATURE MALE
– pursuing a potential mate.

FEMALE egg-laying.

Behaviour – Males set up a temporary beat, patrolling at about head height. If a female is not found after about 20 mins he will move to another part of the water to try his luck.

Habitat – Wide variety of habitats. On ponds, lakes, slow flowing rivers, canals and ditches.

Often found with – The common damselflies, Migrant and Common Hawker and Common Darter.

Females are solitary in their egg-laying, placing them into water plants or damp wood, above and below the water-line. The eggs are diapause and develop over 3 years.

Family CORDULIIDAE

Downy Emerald

Cordulia aenea

Similar species – Brilliant and Northern Emerald.
In flight, superficially like Four-spotted Chaser.
Jizz – Metallic, unobtrusive, fast flyer.
Size – L-48mm, W-69mm
Flight period – Early May – early July
Status – Scarce (3,7,27,37,45,74,96,103,108).
First impression – Medium sized. Dull and downy,
the least metallic of the emeralds. A little bigger than
most of the darters and chasers.

All three emeralds are worth seeking
out and admiring. You will not be
disappointed by them.
Downy is the dullest looking, Brilliant is the
brightest and Northern the darkest.
Downy is the commonest of the
three. They have a scattered
nationwide distribution.

Very downy thorax.

Bright green eyes.

MATURE MALE
Become scruffier
with age.

Abdomen metallic bronze/green, waisted, giving a
clubbed shaped appearance.

C.p. the shape of the anal
appendages, when perched.
Downy E. – short.

Brilliant E. – long.

Northern E. – calliper shaped.

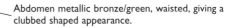

94

Habitat – Neutral to mildly acidic pools, lakes, and canals. Sometimes in slow flowing streams and small rivers. In Scotland in small, peaty lakes in low heather moorland.

Often found with – Brilliant Emerald, Emerald and more common damselflies, Emperor Dragonfly, Broad-bodied and Four-spotted Chaser.

Behaviour – A female is quickly seized by a male when she flies into a territory, the pair fly off in tandem into the tree tops, for well over an hour. They both return to the pond, the male to continue patrolling and the female to egg-lay. She does this by tapping the end of her abdomen into the water to wash the eggs off. The preferred area is amongst marginal emergent vegetation, where there is leaf litter in the water for the larvae to hide in and develop over the next two years.

MATURE FEMALE
– egg-laying.

Female abdomen broader than male. Narrow yellow stripes on segment 2.

ook for them at tree-lined ponds. Males patrol low own for long periods, often in the sheltered margins f the pond. When they need to rest they tend to ettle on bushes or trees a little way from water. If ou notice a male break away from his beat, he is orth following because you may be rewarded with a uperb close-up view. Females can also be seen away om water in woodland.

95

Family CORDULIIDAE
Brilliant Emerald
Somatochlora metallica

Similar species – Downy and Northern Emerald.
Jizz – Dazzling, metallic, elegant.
Size – L-53mm, W-78mm
Flight period – Early Jun – mid Aug
Status – Rare (37,45,62,103,108).
First impression – Medium sized. A stunning,
colourful, metallic dragonfly, fantastic if the sun
catches them.

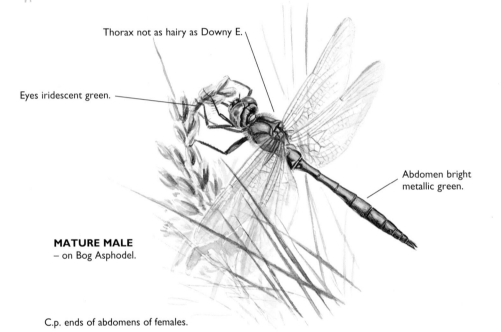

Thorax not as hairy as Downy E.

Eyes iridescent green.

Abdomen bright
metallic green.

MATURE MALE
– on Bog Asphodel.

C.p. ends of abdomens of females.

Downy E. – vulvar scale tucked away.

Brilliant E. – long vulvar scale.

Northern E. – vulvar scale angled.

The brightest and most dramatic looking of the emeralds,
Brilliant E. is a glorious species. Slightly larger than the
others, look for Brilliants patrolling at about waist height
along the edges of pools with lush plant growth. They have
a more consistent flight, pausing less to investigate parts of
the pool c.p. with Downy E. They can be seen with
Downy E., though Downy is on the wing earlier in the
season. They are generally not seen with Northern E. as
they have different habitat requirements.

Brilliant E. has two distinct populations, one in South-East
England and the other in Scotland.

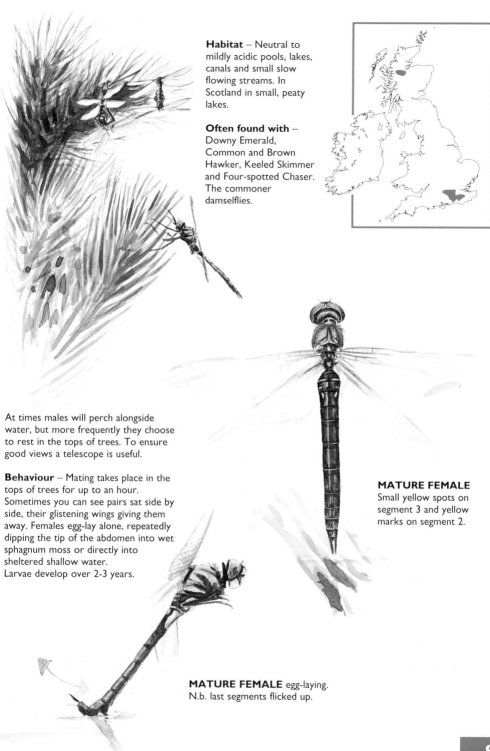

Habitat – Neutral to mildly acidic pools, lakes, canals and small slow flowing streams. In Scotland in small, peaty lakes.

Often found with – Downy Emerald, Common and Brown Hawker, Keeled Skimmer and Four-spotted Chaser. The commoner damselflies.

At times males will perch alongside water, but more frequently they choose to rest in the tops of trees. To ensure good views a telescope is useful.

Behaviour – Mating takes place in the tops of trees for up to an hour. Sometimes you can see pairs sat side by side, their glistening wings giving them away. Females egg-lay alone, repeatedly dipping the tip of the abdomen into wet sphagnum moss or directly into sheltered shallow water.
Larvae develop over 2-3 years.

MATURE FEMALE
Small yellow spots on segment 3 and yellow marks on segment 2.

MATURE FEMALE egg-laying.
N.b. last segments flicked up.

97

Family CORDULIIDAE
Northern Emerald
Somatochlora arctica

Similar species – Downy and Brilliant Emerald.
jizz – Dark, metallic, quick.
Size – L-50mm, W-69mm
Flight period – Early Jun – late Aug
Status – Rare (12, 21).
First impression – Medium sized. Elusive. Dark
with dramatic bright metallic eyes.

Bright green eyes.

Darker green thorax.

Abdomen near black.

A trip to the North-West of Scotland is
needed to see this cracking Dragonfly. It is
possible to have this species in the same field
of view as Azure H., two of Britain's rarest
Dragonflies. They are rare but are possibly
under-recorded because of the vast area in
which they occur.

MATURE MALE

C.p. the distribution of yellow on
the frons and mouthparts.

Downy E.
No yellow on frons.

Brilliant E.
Yellow across frons.

Northern E.
Yellow spots on side
of frons.

Look for them out on bog pools, patrolling
at about waist height. When hunting around
wooded glades they fly steadily, well above
head height, interspersed with bouts of
hovering. Occasionally Northern E. can be
found resting low down in heather. Make
the most of this if they do, because they can
be tricky beasts to get to grips with, the
same with all the emeralds.

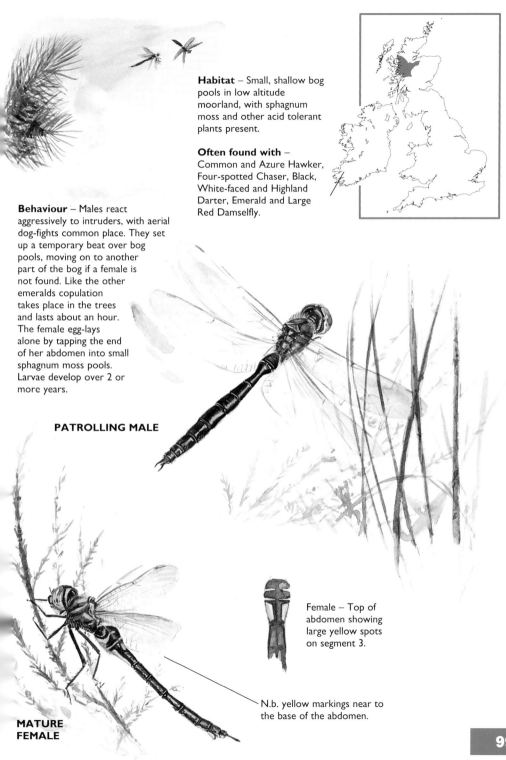

Habitat – Small, shallow bog pools in low altitude moorland, with sphagnum moss and other acid tolerant plants present.

Often found with – Common and Azure Hawker, Four-spotted Chaser, Black, White-faced and Highland Darter, Emerald and Large Red Damselfly.

Behaviour – Males react aggressively to intruders, with aerial dog-fights common place. They set up a temporary beat over bog pools, moving on to another part of the bog if a female is not found. Like the other emeralds copulation takes place in the trees and lasts about an hour. The female egg-lays alone by tapping the end of her abdomen into small sphagnum moss pools. Larvae develop over 2 or more years.

PATROLLING MALE

MATURE FEMALE

Female – Top of abdomen showing large yellow spots on segment 3.

N.b. yellow markings near to the base of the abdomen.

Family LIBELLULIDAE

Four-spotted Chaser

Libellula quadrimaculata

Similar species – Superficially like Downy Emerald.
Jizz – Restless, bustling, fast flyer.
Size – L-43mm, W-76mm
Flight period – Mid May – mid Aug
Status – Very widespread.
First impression – Medium sized. The wing spots stand out at rest. Dull in colour but not behaviour.

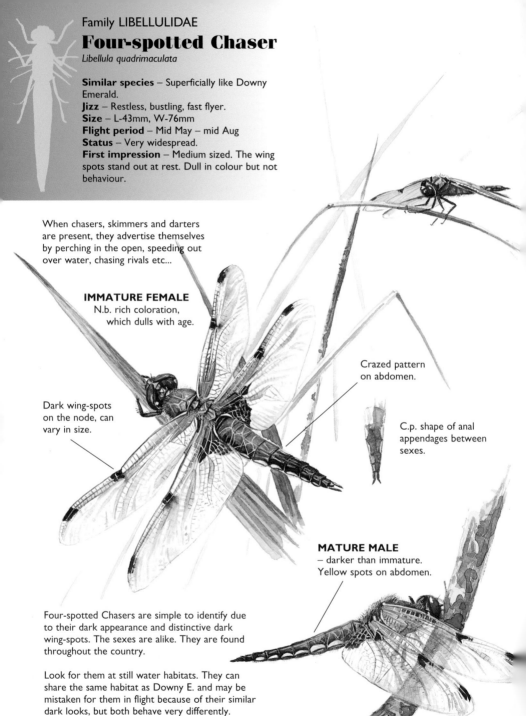

When chasers, skimmers and darters are present, they advertise themselves by perching in the open, speeding out over water, chasing rivals etc...

IMMATURE FEMALE
N.b. rich coloration, which dulls with age.

Crazed pattern on abdomen.

Dark wing-spots on the node, can vary in size.

C.p. shape of anal appendages between sexes.

MATURE MALE
– darker than immature. Yellow spots on abdomen.

Four-spotted Chasers are simple to identify due to their dark appearance and distinctive dark wing-spots. The sexes are alike. They are found throughout the country.

Look for them at still water habitats. They can share the same habitat as Downy E. and may be mistaken for them in flight because of their similar dark looks, but both behave very differently.

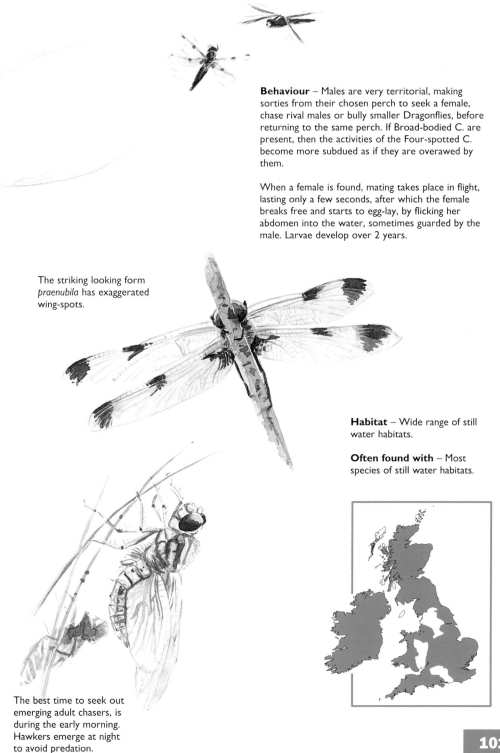

Behaviour – Males are very territorial, making sorties from their chosen perch to seek a female, chase rival males or bully smaller Dragonflies, before returning to the same perch. If Broad-bodied C. are present, then the activities of the Four-spotted C. become more subdued as if they are overawed by them.

When a female is found, mating takes place in flight, lasting only a few seconds, after which the female breaks free and starts to egg-lay, by flicking her abdomen into the water, sometimes guarded by the male. Larvae develop over 2 years.

The striking looking form *praenubila* has exaggerated wing-spots.

Habitat – Wide range of still water habitats.

Often found with – Most species of still water habitats.

The best time to seek out emerging adult chasers, is during the early morning. Hawkers emerge at night to avoid predation.

Family LIBELLULIDAE
Scarce Chaser
Libellula fulva

Similar species – Broad-bodied Chaser, Keeled and Black-tailed Skimmer.
Jizz – Busy, alert, beautiful.
Size – L-44mm, W-75mm
Flight period – Late May – late July
Status – Rare (74,91,111,122).
First impression – Medium sized. Older males have very pale eyes that stand out like "foglights". The orange and black markings of females and young males are stunning.

When perched the chasers tuck the front legs up behind their eyes, this enables them to have greater flexibility for looking around.

Legs tucked up.

A visit to a Scarce Chaser site will leave you feeling as if you have witnessed something special. Their world is that of slow flowing rivers with dense emergent vegetation, where they can be found basking out on Umbellifers and Yellow Iris.

MATURE MALE
Eyes become whiter with age and stand out like "foglights" in flight.

Dark wing bases.

Last 3 segments black.

Smoky wing-spots.

Scarce C. is the rarest of the chasers. Male Keeled S. and Broad-bodied C. differ from Scarce C. by not normally having any black at the end of the abdomen. Black-tailed S. differs by having clear bases to the wings. A bright female or immature male will leave you astounded, they have distinctive abdominal markings. Scarce C. have a scattered south and east distribution.

MATURING MALE

Brown eyes.

Maturing males develop a blue pruinescence – a waxy secretion. This can be worn-off through mating, resulting in dark marks on the middle segments.

102

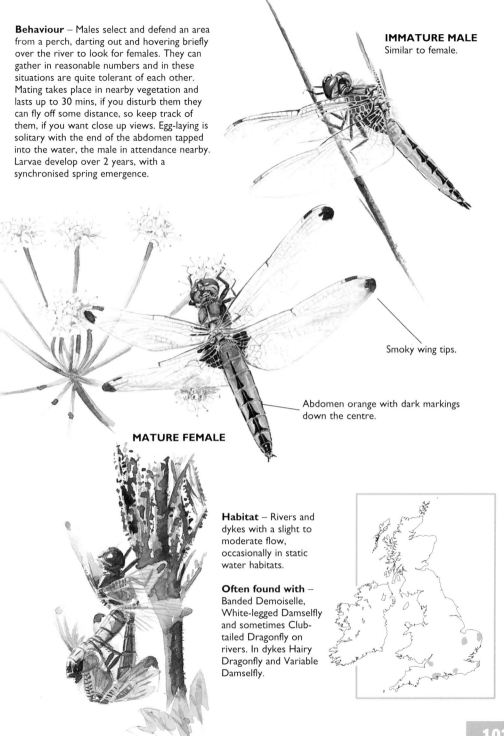

Behaviour – Males select and defend an area from a perch, darting out and hovering briefly over the river to look for females. They can gather in reasonable numbers and in these situations are quite tolerant of each other. Mating takes place in nearby vegetation and lasts up to 30 mins, if you disturb them they can fly off some distance, so keep track of them, if you want close up views. Egg-laying is solitary with the end of the abdomen tapped into the water, the male in attendance nearby. Larvae develop over 2 years, with a synchronised spring emergence.

IMMATURE MALE
Similar to female.

Smoky wing tips.

Abdomen orange with dark markings down the centre.

MATURE FEMALE

Habitat – Rivers and dykes with a slight to moderate flow, occasionally in static water habitats.

Often found with – Banded Demoiselle, White-legged Damselfly and sometimes Club-tailed Dragonfly on rivers. In dykes Hairy Dragonfly and Variable Damselfly.

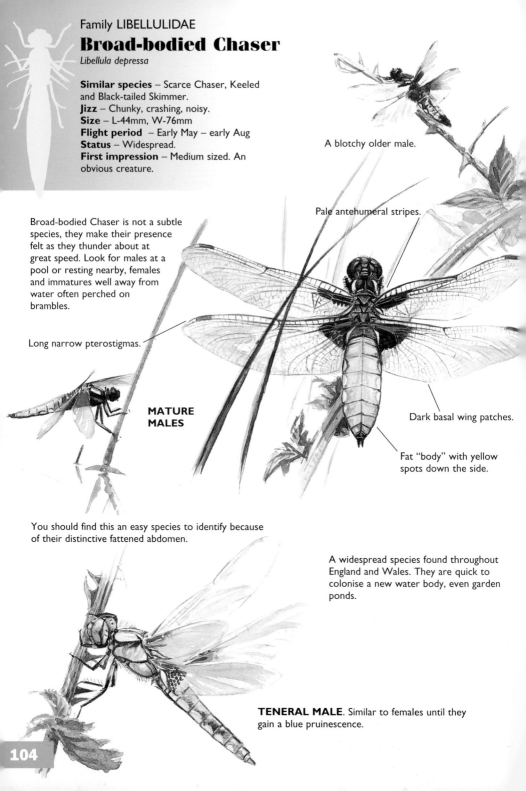

Family LIBELLULIDAE
Broad-bodied Chaser
Libellula depressa

Similar species – Scarce Chaser, Keeled and Black-tailed Skimmer.
Jizz – Chunky, crashing, noisy.
Size – L-44mm, W-76mm
Flight period – Early May – early Aug
Status – Widespread.
First impression – Medium sized. An obvious creature.

A blotchy older male.

Pale antehumeral stripes.

Broad-bodied Chaser is not a subtle species, they make their presence felt as they thunder about at great speed. Look for males at a pool or resting nearby, females and immatures well away from water often perched on brambles.

Long narrow pterostigmas.

MATURE MALES

Dark basal wing patches.

Fat "body" with yellow spots down the side.

You should find this an easy species to identify because of their distinctive fattened abdomen.

A widespread species found throughout England and Wales. They are quick to colonise a new water body, even garden ponds.

TENERAL MALE. Similar to females until they gain a blue pruinescence.

104

Behaviour – On a hot sunny day take the time to sit and watch them. Males are the bullies of a pond, aggressively flying up from a perch to chase off rivals and other species. Females are quickly grasped in flight and just as quickly mated with. Females egg-lay alone with males jealously guarding them. The eggs are washed off by the abdomen, being flicked into the water. Larvae develop over 2 years.

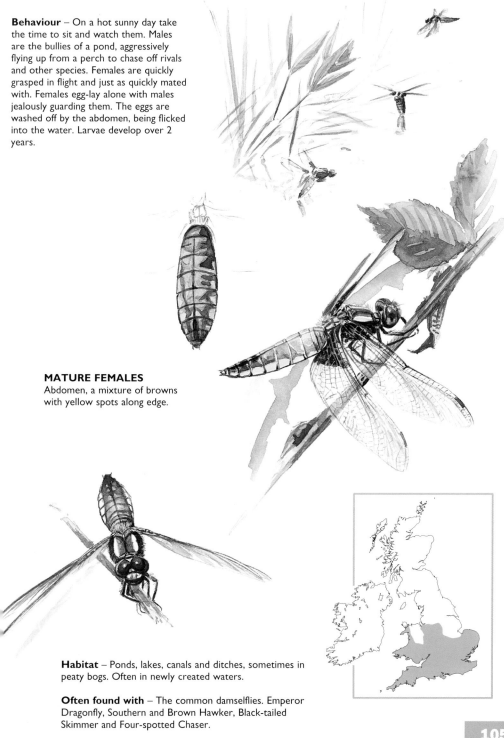

MATURE FEMALES
Abdomen, a mixture of browns with yellow spots along edge.

Habitat – Ponds, lakes, canals and ditches, sometimes in peaty bogs. Often in newly created waters.

Often found with – The common damselflies. Emperor Dragonfly, Southern and Brown Hawker, Black-tailed Skimmer and Four-spotted Chaser.

105

Black-tailed Skimmer

Orthetrum cancellatum

Similar species – Broad-bodied and Scarce Chaser, Keeled Skimmer.
Jizz – Jaggy, skidding flight, fast, aggressive.
Size – L-50mm, W-78mm
Flight period – Mid May – early Aug
Status – Local (37,52,54,58,69,101,114,118).
First impression – Medium sized. The slim structure and black tail of the male stands out, along with the dramatic patterns on the immature males and females.

Look for basking males on open areas of dry mud and shingle, close to a water body. You will find that they flush from under your feet. Immature males and females tend to be further afield.

Black-tailed Skimmer is most similar to Scarce C., however Black-tailed S. have clear wing bases and the abdomen has yellow spots along the edge, which turn blue with age. They have a southerly distribution.

No antehumeral stripes on thorax.

MATURE MALE

Clear wings.

Abdomen blue, tipped black. Yellow spots along edge.

Pale eyes.

A striking **IMMATURE MALE**, similar to female.

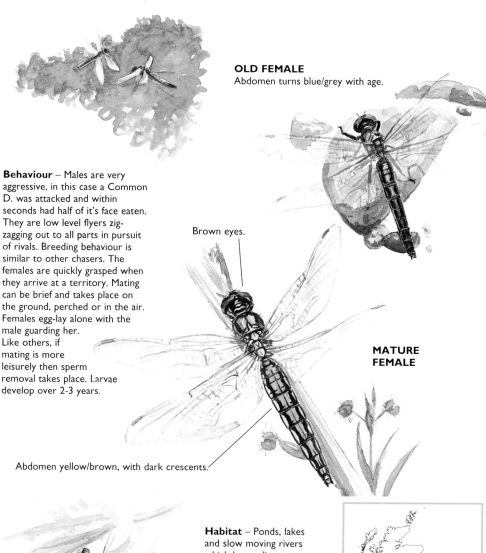

OLD FEMALE
Abdomen turns blue/grey with age.

Behaviour – Males are very
aggressive, in this case a Common
D. was attacked and within
seconds had half of it's face eaten.
They are low level flyers zig-
zagging out to all parts in pursuit
of rivals. Breeding behaviour is
similar to other chasers. The
females are quickly grasped when
they arrive at a territory. Mating
can be brief and takes place on
the ground, perched or in the air.
Females egg-lay alone with the
male guarding her.
Like others, if
mating is more
leisurely then sperm
removal takes place. Larvae
develop over 2-3 years.

Brown eyes.

**MATURE
FEMALE**

Abdomen yellow/brown, with dark crescents.

Habitat – Ponds, lakes
and slow moving rivers
which have adjacent
bare ground on which
to settle. In Ireland
often in marl lakes in
limestone areas.

Often found with –
The common
damselflies. Hairy and
Emperor Dragonfly and
Broad-bodied Chaser.

Family LIBELLULIDAE
Keeled Skimmer
Orthetrum coerulescens

Similar species – Scarce and Broad-bodied Chaser, Black-tailed Skimmer.
Jizz – Excitable, slender, feisty.
Size – L-42mm, W-60mm
Flight period – Mid June – late Aug
Status – Local (8,25,30,53,68,103).
First impression – Medium sized. A perky species.

MATURE FEMALE

Look for them sat low down on plants or sunning themselves on the ground along an acidic stream. Sometimes newly emerged adults can be found in large numbers on nearby heathland.

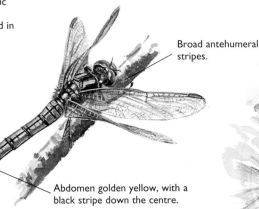

Broad antehumeral stripes.

Abdomen golden yellow, with a black stripe down the centre.

They will be nervous of you when you first enter their habitat, but if you move slowly they will soon treat you as part of the scenery.

Clear wings.

Males defend a small territory, challenging invaders, even Golden-ringed D.

Tip normally blue, though it can become black through the rigours of mating

Abdomen slim pale blue.

MATURE MALE

Behaviour – Females are quickly grasped as they enter a territory and the pair will fly off into nearby bushes to mate. Mating can be leisurely. You might see pairs flying in tandem apparently egg-laying, it is likely to be inexperienced pairs, searching for suitable sites. More often females egg-lay alone, sometimes guarded by the male. Larvae develop over 2 years.

OLDER MALE
Cleaning eyes with legs.
N.b. blue on thorax.

Habitat – Acidic flushes and streams, valley mires and sphagnum pools in heathland and moorland areas.

Often found with –
Beautiful Demoiselle, Southern, Small Red and Large Red Damselfly. Common Hawker and Golden-ringed Dragonfly.

TENERAL MALE

Family LIBELLULIDAE

Common Darter

Sympetrum striolatum

Similar Species – Ruddy, Red-veined and Highland Darter.
Jizz – Bold, inquisitive, slender.
Size – L-37mm, W-57mm
Flight period – Mid June – end Oct
Status – Very widespread.
First impression – Small. Where present there always seems to be a busy atmosphere. A bright species, males are orange/red in colour, females yellow.

They can be found at most water bodies. Sat out on the ground to gain warmth or perched conspicuously on a twig.

IMMATURE MALE. Look for these away from water in woodland.

MATURE MALE

Legs black with yellow.

Abdomen orange/red.

Widespread throughout England and Wales, Common Darter is similar to Ruddy D., which is smaller, club shaped and has black legs with no yellow on them. Highland D. is very similar, but is richer in colour and is found further north only in Scotland.

They are quite likely to turn up in your garden, this one is using a washing line as a perch.

End of abdomen curves down showing that he has recently been mating.

Black line along top of frons only.

MATURE MALE

C.p. side of thorax with Highland and Ruddy D.

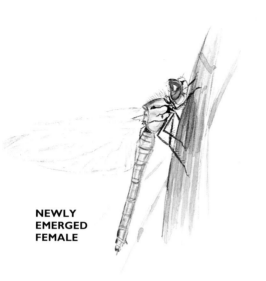

NEWLY EMERGED FEMALE

HIGHLAND DARTER

COMMON DARTER

Habitat – Wide range of habitats.

Often found with – Most other southern based Dragonflies.

MATURE FEMALE

Antehumeral stripes on the thorax are variable in width and are sometimes absent.

Abdomen yellow with black darts.

Behaviour – Strangely some males are fiercely territorial chasing anything that flies. While others will sit placidly within these territories without being hassled, by the more aggressive males. Look up at a pool and you may see other males hovering above you. They are unable to hold a territory and are waiting to grab females as they fly upwards from a pond after egg-laying.

OLDER FEMALE
Taking on the red colours of males.

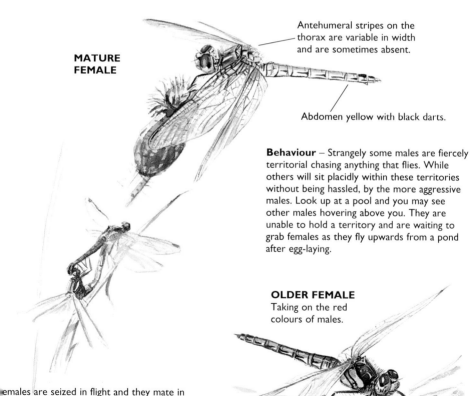

...emales are seized in flight and they mate in ...earby vegetation. After about 10 mins the ...air egg-lay in tandem, dipping into the water ... wash off the eggs. It is not unusual to see ...any pairs flying around a pond at one time. ...ome females egg-lay alone. Larvae develop ...ver a year.

Highland Darter

Sympetrum nigrescens

Similar species – Common Darter.
Jizz – Unafraid, busy, slim.
Size – L-37mm, W-57mm
Flight period – Early July – early Oct
Status – Scarce (21,31).
First impression – Small. A darker, richer version of Common Darter, males similar in colour to Ruddy Darter. Exaggerated markings.

IMMATURE MALE. N.b. black down the side of the frons.

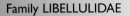

N.b. extensive black markings on the side of the thorax.

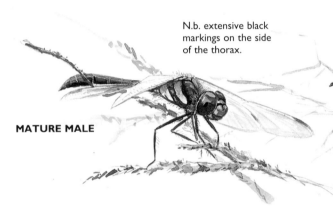

MATURE MALE

The controversial "lumping and splitting" of species that dogs modern day birding, is reflected here with this insect. Is Highland Darter a true species or just a dark form of Common Darter? They are certainly much darker in colour. As a rule all Common Darters found to the north of Glasgow are true Highland Darters. Those found in south-west Scotland are questionable. It is certainly worth looking out for this species and making your own mind up.

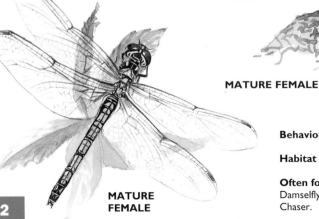

MATURE FEMALE

MATURE FEMALE

Behaviour – Similar to that of Common D.

Habitat – Wide range of habitats.

Often found with – Emerald and Large Red Damselfly. Common Hawker and Four-spotted Chaser.

Comparison of the amount of black on the frons between three very similar darters.

Highland Darter.
Black down side of frons.

Vagrant Darter.
Black slightly down side of frons.

Common Darter.
Black along top of frons only.

Abdomen shapes of blue chasers.

Broad-bodied Chaser.
Fat. With yellow spots. Tip can become worn black.

Scarce Chaser.
No yellow spots. Black on last 3 segments.

Black-tailed Skimmer.
Yellow spots. May turn blue with age. Extensive black on tip.

Keeled Skimmer.
Slender. Pale blue. Tip can become worn black.

Family LIBELLULIDAE

Ruddy Darter

Sympetrum sanguineum

Similar species – Common Darter.
Jizz – Fidgety, flitting, endearing.
Size – L-34mm, W-55mm
Flight period – Late Jun – end Oct
Status – Widespread.
First impression – Smaller than Common Darter. Rich blood-red colouring in males, females yellow ochre. The pinched "waist" of males is obvious.

MATURE MALE
"sky-pointing". In very hot weather darters adopt this curious posture, in order to prevent themselves over-heating.

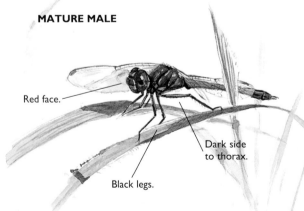

MATURE MALE

Brown thorax.

Abdomen club shaped.

MATURE MALE

Red face.

Dark side to thorax.

Black legs.

Ruddy Darter is the smallest of the red darters. Take care when first sorting this species out, because they are likely to be seen and confused with Common D. Male Ruddy D. are a deep red, not orange/red, they lack markings on the thorax and have a red face. Female Ruddy D. differ from female Common D. by having fewer black markings on the thorax and like males have black legs with no yellow on them.

Initially Ruddy Darters will be cautious of you, but in a short time you will find yourself readily accepted by them. They are good fun to watch and may even sit on your pen as you make notes.

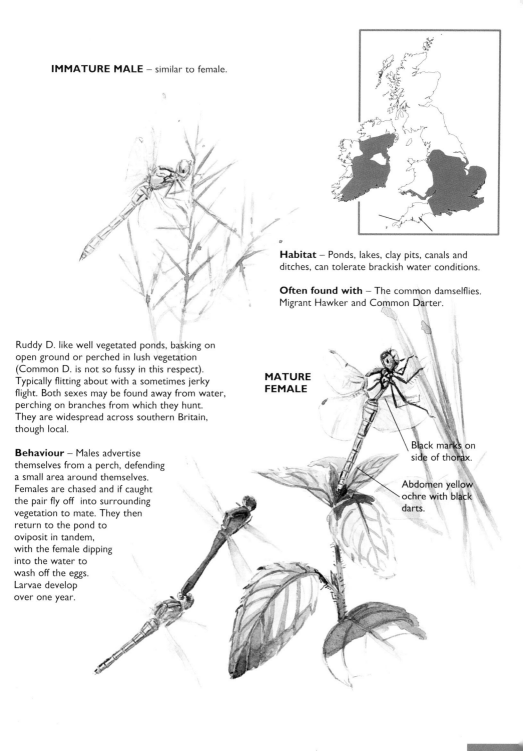

IMMATURE MALE – similar to female.

Habitat – Ponds, lakes, clay pits, canals and ditches, can tolerate brackish water conditions.

Often found with – The common damselflies. Migrant Hawker and Common Darter.

Ruddy D. like well vegetated ponds, basking on open ground or perched in lush vegetation (Common D. is not so fussy in this respect). Typically flitting about with a sometimes jerky flight. Both sexes may be found away from water, perching on branches from which they hunt. They are widespread across southern Britain, though local.

Behaviour – Males advertise themselves from a perch, defending a small area around themselves. Females are chased and if caught the pair fly off into surrounding vegetation to mate. They then return to the pond to oviposit in tandem, with the female dipping into the water to wash off the eggs. Larvae develop over one year.

MATURE FEMALE

Black marks on side of thorax.

Abdomen yellow ochre with black darts.

115

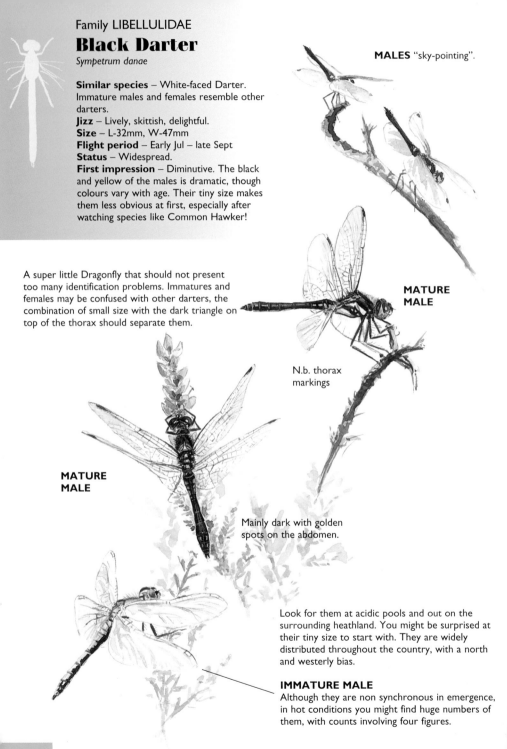

Family LIBELLULIDAE

Black Darter
Sympetrum danae

Similar species – White-faced Darter.
Immature males and females resemble other
darters.
Jizz – Lively, skittish, delightful.
Size – L-32mm, W-47mm
Flight period – Early Jul – late Sept
Status – Widespread.
First impression – Diminutive. The black
and yellow of the males is dramatic, though
colours vary with age. Their tiny size makes
them less obvious at first, especially after
watching species like Common Hawker!

MALES "sky-pointing".

A super little Dragonfly that should not present
too many identification problems. Immatures and
females may be confused with other darters, the
combination of small size with the dark triangle on
top of the thorax should separate them.

MATURE
MALE

N.b. thorax
markings

MATURE
MALE

Mainly dark with golden
spots on the abdomen.

Look for them at acidic pools and out on the
surrounding heathland. You might be surprised at
their tiny size to start with. They are widely
distributed throughout the country, with a north
and westerly bias.

IMMATURE MALE
Although they are non synchronous in emergence,
in hot conditions you might find huge numbers of
them, with counts involving four figures.

Habitat – Boggy pools, old peat cuttings, peaty ponds and acidic fens on heaths and moorland.

Often found with – Emerald Damselfly, other common damselflies, Common Hawker and White-faced Darter.

N.b. thorax markings.

MATURE FEMALES

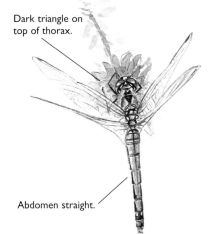

Dark triangle on top of thorax.

Black legs.

Abdomen straight.

Behaviour – Breeding behaviour is different from other darters in that the males search for a mate. This may involve a group of males chasing after a female, with the fittest winning the prize, or individuals seeking a mate hidden in the heather. The pair mate sat in vegetation, after which they egg-lay in tandem, though you may find some females egg-laying alone with the male in attendance. The eggs are diapause, with the larvae developing during the following season.

Family LIBELLULIDAE

White-faced Darter
Leucorrhinia dubia

Similar species – Black Darter.
Jizz – Excitable crackerjacks.
Size – L-37mm, W-52mm
Flight period – Mid May – early Aug
Status – Rare (17,27,117).
First impression – Small, slightly bigger than Black Darter. Incredibly jizzy, jerky flight. Look like their faces have been dipped into a pot of off-white paint. This feature stands out.

IMMATURE MALE

N.b. off-white frons.

MATURE MALE – in threat posture.

Another "must see" species.
Look for them at peaty pools, typically perched on sphagnum moss, dead wood and white shirts. If you disturb them too much they may flush up into nearby trees. The males appear dark, with deep red to orange spots. Immature males resemble harlequins with their black and white markings, and are similar to females. Both sexes display a striking off-white face. They maybe confused with Black D. because of their small size, but the markings are completely different.

MATURE MALE
Abdomen black with deep red to orange spots.

They have been severely threatened by the destruction of their habitat in recent years, the major culprits being the drainage of bogs and the commercial collection of moss for hanging baskets.

Behaviour – Males loosely interact with other males at the breeding area, but when basking on bare logs they are very tolerant of each other. Females only come to the pool to mate and are soon clasped when they arrive. The pair fly to low growing plants or onto bare logs to mate. Mating lasts up to half an hour. If other males come too close to a pair "in cop", the male reacts by vibrating his wings.

Habitat – Acidic bog pools with no fish and large amounts of sphagnum moss.

Often found with – Emerald and Large Red Damselfly, Common Hawker, Four-spotted Chaser, Black Darter, and in Scotland sometimes Northern Damselfly.

The female returns to the pool to egg-lay by continually tapping her abdomen into open patches of water between sphagnum moss, the male hovering close by. The larvae develop over 2 years with a synchronous spring emergence.

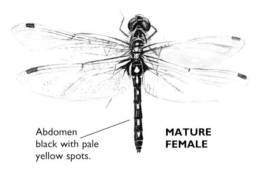

Abdomen black with pale yellow spots.

MATURE FEMALE

White-faced D. fly in a jerky "war dance" fashion.

They have a scattered distribution, the stronghold being North Scotland, with other population's in North-West England and the Welsh borders.

119

Family LIBELLULIDAE
Yellow-winged Darter
Sympetrum flaveolum

Similar species – Other red darters.
Jizz – Flying tangerines.
Size – L-34mm, W-55mm
Flight period – A late summer migrant.
Status – Vagrant, possible coloniser.

Prior to 1995 there had only been a handful of records. The invasion of August 1995 involved 100's of this species spread over 30 counties. Since then there has been successful breeding at a few sites. They are usually found in Europe. Yellow-winged D. are not only to be found near water, but also more frequently well away from water.

MATURE MALE

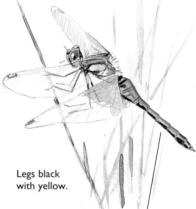

Legs black with yellow.

Strongly marked black on side of abdomen.

MATURE MALE

Conspicuous golden-yellow patches.

MATURE FEMALE

MATURE FEMALE

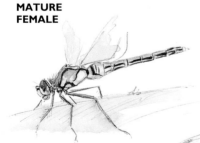

Wing patches not as bright as males.

Family LIBELLULIDAE
Red-veined Darter
Sympetrum fonscolombii

Similar species – Other red darters.
Jizz – Strong, powerful.
Size – L-40mm, W-63mm
Flight period – June – Aug
Status – Vagrant, probable coloniser.

Larger, more robust than Common D and Ruddy D.

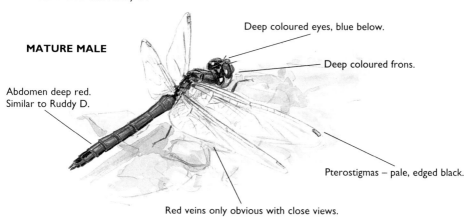

MATURE MALE

Deep coloured eyes, blue below.

Deep coloured frons.

Abdomen deep red. Similar to Ruddy D.

Pterostigmas – pale, edged black.

Red veins only obvious with close views.

Abdomen – yellow-ochre.

MATURE FEMALE

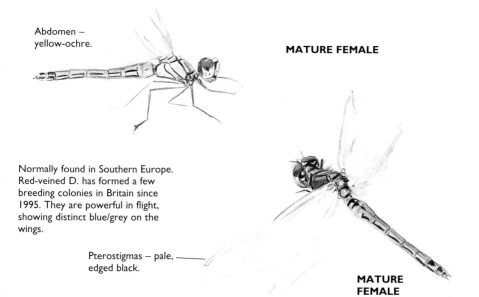

Normally found in Southern Europe. Red-veined D. has formed a few breeding colonies in Britain since 1995. They are powerful in flight, showing distinct blue/grey on the wings.

Pterostigmas – pale, edged black.

MATURE FEMALE

Vagrants I

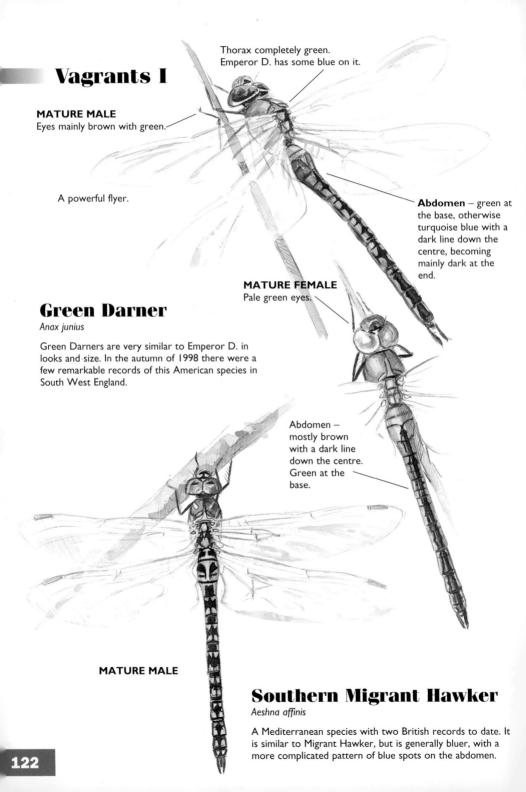

Thorax completely green.
Emperor D. has some blue on it.

MATURE MALE
Eyes mainly brown with green.

A powerful flyer.

Abdomen – green at
the base, otherwise
turquoise blue with a
dark line down the
centre, becoming
mainly dark at the
end.

MATURE FEMALE
Pale green eyes.

Green Darner
Anax junius

Green Darners are very similar to Emperor D. in
looks and size. In the autumn of 1998 there were a
few remarkable records of this American species in
South West England.

Abdomen –
mostly brown
with a dark line
down the centre.
Green at the
base.

MATURE MALE

Southern Migrant Hawker
Aeshna affinis

A Mediterranean species with two British records to date. It
is similar to Migrant Hawker, but is generally bluer, with a
more complicated pattern of blue spots on the abdomen.

Lesser Emperor
Anax parthenope

Usually found in Southern Europe with three British records to date, Lesser Emperor is a powerful and manoeuvrable beast slightly smaller in size c.p. to Emperor D.

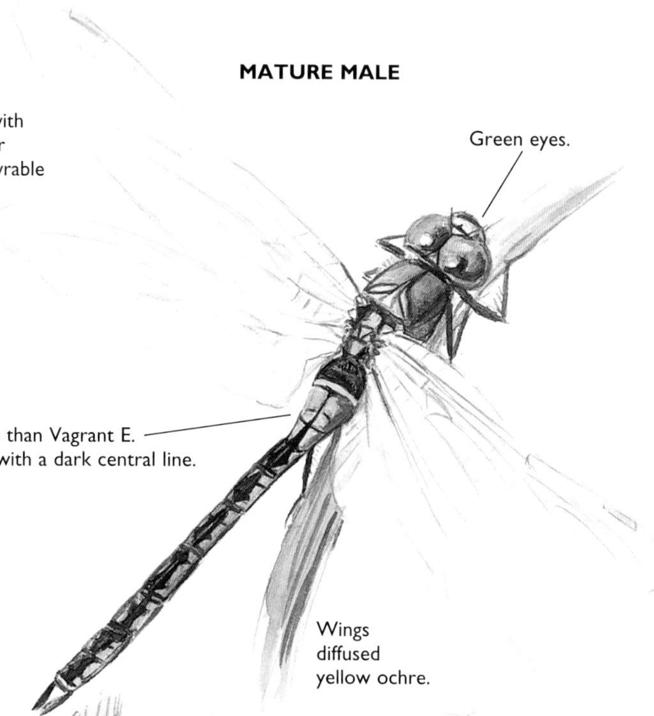

MATURE MALE

Green eyes.

Pale blue "saddle" more extensive than Vagrant E.
Abdomen – straight, dark brown with a dark central line.

Wings diffused yellow ochre.

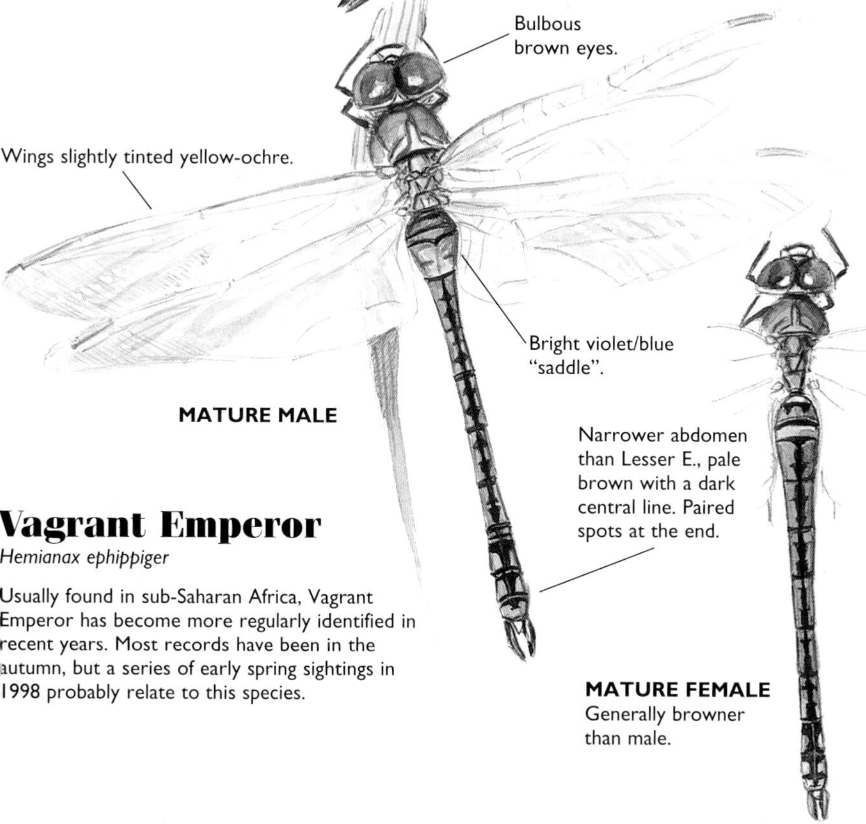

Bulbous brown eyes.

Wings slightly tinted yellow-ochre.

Bright violet/blue "saddle".

MATURE MALE

Vagrant Emperor
Hemianax ephippiger

Usually found in sub-Saharan Africa, Vagrant Emperor has become more regularly identified in recent years. Most records have been in the autumn, but a series of early spring sightings in 1998 probably relate to this species.

Narrower abdomen than Lesser E., pale brown with a dark central line. Paired spots at the end.

MATURE FEMALE
Generally browner than male.

Vagrants II

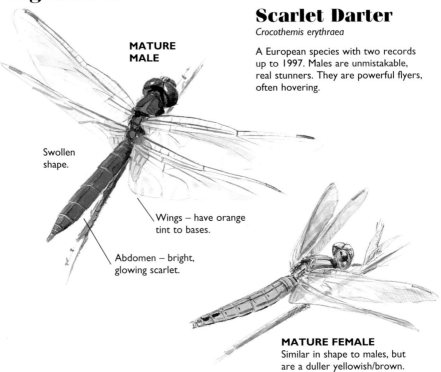

MATURE MALE

Scarlet Darter
Crocothemis erythraea

A European species with two records up to 1997. Males are unmistakable, real stunners. They are powerful flyers, often hovering.

Swollen shape.

Wings – have orange tint to bases.

Abdomen – bright, glowing scarlet.

MATURE FEMALE
Similar in shape to males, but are a duller yellowish/brown.

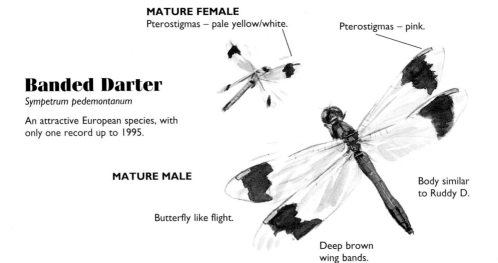

MATURE FEMALE
Pterostigmas – pale yellow/white.

Pterostigmas – pink.

Banded Darter
Sympetrum pedemontanum

An attractive European species, with only one record up to 1995.

MATURE MALE

Butterfly like flight.

Body similar to Ruddy D.

Deep brown wing bands.

Vagrant Darter
Sympetrum vulgatum

Vagrant Darter is a rare, irregular migrant from Europe. They are very similar to Common D., the distinguishing features being, that the black extends down the side of the frons with Vagrant D. and is only found on the top of the frons with Common D. Females show a prominent vulvar scale. Ruddy D. also has black extending down the side of the frons, but has distinctive black legs.

MATURE MALE

Black extends down side of frons.

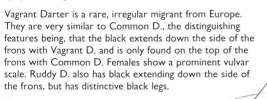

Legs black and yellow.

Thorax — less well marked than Common D.

Abdomen slightly club-shaped.

Female black central line on abdomen.

N.b. distinctive vulvar scale.

Globe Skimmer
Pantala flavescens

Globe Skimmer is a long range migrant usually found in tropical areas on both sides of the Atlantic. There have been four records up to 1989. You may pick one out at a distance by it's jizzy gliding flight.

MATURE MALE

Southern Skimmer
Orthetrum brunneum

A report in 1995 probably relates to this very distinctive South European species.

MATURE MALE
Body virtually all pale powder blue.
N.b. some mature male Keeled Skimmers are all blue, but are smaller in size and not so robust.

Broad hind wings, tinted yellow at base.

Abdomen — yellow/red, with a dark centre.

FEMALES are generally yellow-ochre in colour.

125

Index